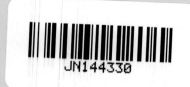

BASIC ENGLISH TEXTBOOK FOR LEARNERS OF REHABILITATION SCIENCES, 3RD EDITION

リハビリテーションの基礎英語

第3版

■企画・構成・編著 清水雅子 ■英文監修 Timothy Minton ■PT・OT監修 三木貴弘, 上 梓

MEDICAL VIEW

Basic English Textbook for Learners of Rehabilitation Sciences, 3rd edition
(ISBN 978-4-7583-0961-5 C3047)

Editorial Author: Masako Shimizu
English Supervisor: Timothy Minton
PT, OT Supervisors: Takahiro Miki, Azusa Kami

2009. 4. 10 1st ed.
2016. 1. 1 revised ed.
2017. 4. 1 3rd ed.

Printed and Bound in Japan

Medical View Co., Ltd.
2-30 Ichigaya-hommuracho, Shinjuku-ku, Tokyo, 162-0845, Japan
E-mail ed@medicalview.co.jp

第3版刊行にあたって

本書『リハビリテーションの基礎英語』の初版（2009年）を刊行してから，約8年が経過いたしました。この間に，リハビリテーション医療英語へのニーズは一段と高まってきたように思われます。リハビリテーション医療を取りまく社会状況は変化の一途を辿っております。特に日本は，世界における長寿国ナンバーワンとなって久しく，それに伴って，高齢者の心身の変化に対応するリハビリテーションが必要とされてきました。同時に，障害者のみならず，脳卒中や心臓病などの生活習慣による慢性疾患および癌の急増は，健康長寿をめざす人々にとって重大な問題となっています。さらに社会的ストレスによる心因性疾患の増加も加わり，広範囲にわたるリハビリテーション医療が期待されています。

一方，2014年，WHOが提唱した「障害者の権利に関する条約」を批准した日本には，リハビリテーション職種に携わる人々の国際協力への積極的な参加，さらには指導力の発揮が強く求められています。このような状況下にあって，理学療法士・作業療法士・言語聴覚士が国際社会で活躍するには外国語，特に英語習得が必要です。それは，海外における活動だけでなく，国際交流が一般的になった国内においても例外ではありません。

第3版では，このような背景を考慮して，新たに学習者がより取り組みやすくなるように，内容の検討および英文の変更を行いました。本書がきっかけとなり，多くの方が将来，より高度な専門英語へと移行されることを願っております。

本書の改訂にあたり，専門分野の見地から，札幌円山整形外科病院リハビリテーション科 三木貴弘氏，笹川スポーツ財団スポーツ政策研究所 上 梓氏に貴重なご助言，ご教示をいただきました。また英語表現に関しましては，慶應義塾大学医学部 Timothy Minton教授に，全般にわたり綿密なご校閲をいただきました。ここに深く感謝申し上げます。

なお，メジカルビュー社 高橋 学氏には，編集の立場から貴重なご助言をいただき，さらには，細部の校正に至るまで大変お世話になりました。心からお礼申し上げます。

2017年1月

清水 雅子

第2版刊行にあたって

本書は，拙著『リハビリテーションの基礎英語』（2009年刊）の内容を新たな視点から見直し，改訂したものです。

本書の初版出版後，約7年の間に，リハビリテーション医療を取りまく社会状況はかなり変化しています。生活習慣病による慢性疾患や社会的ストレスによる心因性疾患などの増加，地域社会における高齢者の急増，国内外を問わず起きる大災害など，広範囲にわたりリハビリテーション医療へのニーズはますます高まっています。そのニーズには，心身の障害が可能なかぎり元の状態に戻るようにリハビリを行うことはもとより，障害をもったままでもよりよい人生を送るための温かい支援も含まれています。一歩進んで，予防医学の観点から，日常生活に運動や趣味を取り入れたQOLを重んじる支援も重要になっています。

さらに，日本はWHOが提唱した「障害者の権利に関する条約」を批准し（2014年），リハビリテーション職種に携わる人々の国際協力への積極的な参加，さらにその指導力を発揮することに大きな期待が寄せられています。

このような状況にあって，理学療法士・作業療法士・言語聴覚士はもちろんのこと，チーム医療に携わる他の専門職種の人々も，国際社会で活躍するには外国語，特に英語習得が必要です。それは，海外における活動だけでなく，国際交流が一般的になった国内においても例外ではありません。

このような背景を考慮して，第2版では新たに導入として「運動と身体」を，第4章「病気とリハビリテーション」に「脊髄損傷」「言語障害」を，そして英和と和英による索引を加えました。

なお，英語学習に欠かせない語彙習得のために，日本語の説明や図版を挿入し，側注やNotesを付記，練習問題によって各事項の学習達成度を知ることができるように工夫しました。しかし，専門英語の学習は単調になりがちです。楽しみながら継続できればと考え，「One Point Lesson」「ことばのルーツ」を掲載しています。本書がきっかけとなり，一人でも多くの方が将来，より高度な専門英語へと移行されることを願っております。

本書の改訂にあたり，引用箇所以外の英語表現に関して，東京医科大学国際医学情報学分野Edward F. Barroga先生に綿密なご校閲をいただきました。深く感謝申し上げます。

なお，メジカルビュー社の江口潤司氏には，編集の立場から貴重なご助言をいただき，さらには，細部の校正に至るまで大変お世話になりました。心からお礼申し上げます。

2015年12月

清水 雅子

第1版刊行にあたって

近年，日本においても障害(傷害)者，高齢者の身体的，心理的，社会的，職業的回復を目指すリハビリテーション医学・医療が注目を浴び，大きな期待が寄せられています。

リハビリテーション医学は，20世紀に入り，二度にわたる世界大戦で負傷した傷病兵の社会復帰に向けた訓練が大きな原動力となり発展してきました。今日このリハビリテーション医学を中心に，リハビリテーション医療は理学療法士，作業療法士，看護師，臨床心理士，職業訓練士，ソーシャルワーカー，義肢装具士などを中心として構成されるチーム医療として，障害のある人たちの個人的回復，社会的復帰を支援する重要な領域となっています。

リハビリテーションという行為は，ラテン語語源の《re-(再び) + habilitas (ある状態に保つ)》が示唆するように，人が人間として生き，社会に復帰する能力・機能を再び獲得することを意味します。さらに，WHO (世界保健機関)の定義では「障害者自身，その家族，そして彼らの住む地域社会はリハビリテーションに関する諸種のサービスの計画と実施に関与しなければならない」と述べられているように，障害者自身もさまざまな支援を受けながら，自分の能力を発揮して，自己実現を図りながら社会で生きていくための復帰努力をすることが必要です。

本書はそのような医療の中で重要な役割を果たす理学療法士，作業療法士に焦点を当てて，リハビリテーションの基礎的事項を英語で学習することを目的に編纂しました。

テキストの各章は以下のような学習目的をもつ内容で構成されています。

Chapter I: What is Rehabilitation? (リハビリテーションとは？)

＊歴史と定義などからリハビリテーションの概念を把握する。

Chapter II: Fundamentals of the Human Body for Rehabilitation (リハビリテーションのための人体の基礎知識)

＊身体的運動に必要な人体に関するルールを習得する。

Chapter III: The Structure of the Human Body (人体の構造)

＊身体的運動に関わる骨格・関節・筋肉・神経系の構造と機能を学習する。

Chapter IV: Diseases and Rehabilitation (病気とリハビリテーション)

＊障害および傷害を引き起こす病気の概略と運動療法の実例を学習する。

Chapter V: A Case of Quadriplegia from Spinal Cord Injury; Juan's Story (脊髄損傷の症例：ファンの場合)

＊事故による脊髄損傷患者が身体的，職業的リハビリテーションによって，人生の目的と生きがいを見出すまでのプロセスを，ファン(Juan) の実例から学ぶ。

Appendix: リハビリテーションに関する略語(英語・日本語)

以上の内容を学習し，必須語彙の習得を容易にするために英文には注を付記し，可能な限り日本語を併記しました。また，図版を多く取り入れ，視覚的に学習できるように特に工夫しました。本書がきっかけとなり，学習者が将来の専門英語にスムーズに移行できるようになることを強く願っています。

本書の執筆にあたり，医学の専門的立場から数々の貴重なご教示・ご助言を賜りました川崎医療福祉大学 長尾光城教授に心から感謝申し上げます。

なお，メジカルビュー社吉川みゆき様，江口潤司様，高橋学様には，立案から校正に至るまで大変お世話になりました。心からお礼申し上げます。

2009年3月

川崎医療福祉大学／大学院
医療福祉学研究科教授

清水 雅子

目次　Contents

WHO（世界保健機関）が定める リハビリテーション

Definition of Rehabilitation (WHO, 1981)

Rehabilitation includes all measures aimed at reducing the impact of disabling and handicapping conditions, and at enabling the disabled and handicapped to achieve social integration.

Rehabilitation aims not only at training disabled and handicapped persons to adapt to their environment, but also at intervening in their immediate environment and society as a whole in order to facilitate their social integration.

The disabled and handicapped themselves, their families, and the communities they live in should be involved in the planning and implementation of services related to rehabilitation.

リハビリテーションの定義 (WHO, 1981)

リハビリテーションとは，能力障害あるいは社会的不利を起こす諸条件の悪影響を減少させ，障害者の社会統合を実現することをめざすあらゆる措置を含むものである。

リハビリテーションは障害者を訓練してその環境に適応させるだけでなく，障害者の直接的環境および社会全体に介入して彼らの社会統合を容易にすることをも目的とする。

障害者自身，その家族，そして彼らの住む地域社会はリハビリテーションに関係する諸種のサービスの計画と実施に関与しなければならない。

INTRODUCTION

Exercise and the Body: Staying Healthy

INTRODUCTION

Exercise and the Body: Staying Healthy
運動と身体：健康を保つために

What is Health? 健康とは

The World Health Organization (WHO)❶ defines health as "a state of complete physical, mental and social well-being and not merely the absence of disease or infirmity.❷" However, many people with physical or mental disabilities might dispute this definition, considering themselves to be healthy in spite of their disabilities. They might well say that a truly healthy person is someone who has a realistic outlook on life and social relationships. What is certainly true is that having a basic knowledge of physical health and the ability to focus on healthy lifestyle choices can help all of us stay healthy❸ and achieve a better quality of life.

Health professionals,❹ particularly physical therapists, occupational therapists, speech and language therapists, and others who are engaged in rehabilitation, need to keep this in mind. Most importantly, health professionals need to have a sound knowledge of the human body and of the lifestyle choices that keep it in good condition, as such knowledge is essential if they are to be successful in helping their patients through the process of rehabilitation.

Let's begin by learning more about the fascinating structure of the human body and the importance of exercise in maintaining health.

健康で幸せな状態

障害
《p.4 Notes 参照》

現実的な人生観

医療従事者

人体の構造

Notes

❶ **The World Health Organization (WHO) 世界保健機関**：1948年設立。本部ジュネーブ。すべての人々に最高水準の保健衛生をもたらすことを基本目的とする機関。活動範囲は広く，感染症・各種疾病への対策，保健要員の訓練，基礎医薬品や予防接種，食糧の充実など多岐にわたる。
The Preamble to the Constitution of the World Health Organization（世界保健機関憲章前文）に「健康とは、病気でないとか、弱っていないということではなく、肉体的にも、精神的にも、そして社会的にも、すべてが満たされた状態にあることをいいます。(日本WHO協会訳)」とある。
前文には，以下の事柄も述べられている。
The extension to all peoples of the benefits of medical, psychological and related knowledge is essential to the fullest attainment of health.（健康を完全に達成するためには，医学，心理学や関連する学問の恩恵をすべての人々に広げることが不可欠です。）

❷ **infirmity (frailty) 虚弱**：(長期にわたる身体的・精神的な)虚弱，あるいは病弱をいう。

❸ **stay healthy　健康なままでいる**：stayは人などがある状態のままでいる(ある)という意味で，remainよりも口語的。補語は形容詞(語句)，分詞，名詞など。

❹ **professional　専門家**：リハビリテーション，その周辺の専門家については，p.14参照。professionの語源は，人々の前で(pro)＝公に，宣言すること(fession)の意味。

EXERCISES

1. 不要なアルファベットを除き，英単語を見つけなさい。

physicalingmentaltasocialtutherapistetoccupational

1 __________　2 __________　3 __________　4 __________　5 __________

2. 英文の内容に合う適切な英語を(　　　)に書き入れなさい。

(1) Health means more than the absence of disease or (　　　).

(2) Having a basic knowledge of (　　　) health and healthy lifestyles helps everyone (　　　) healthy.

(3) Health (　　　) engaged in rehabilitation include (　　　) therapists, (　　　) therapists, and (　　　) therapists.

3. 内容が正しい文にはTを，間違っている文にはFを記入しなさい。

(1) _____ Everyone would agree with WHO's definition of health.

(2) _____ Making healthy lifestyle choices is likely to improve a person's quality of life.

(3) _____ Health professionals will not be able to provide good rehabilitation services without a good knowledge of the human body.

Exercise for Everyone　運動をしよう

　　Health problems are, unfortunately, not uncommon. Nowadays, people tend to spend too much time in sedentary activities like watching television and using computers. In addition, many choose to drive, even when they have more physically active options like cycling. To make matters worse, people all around the world are eating more fast food, fatty meats, and salty snacks. These foods are loaded with calories but lacking in nutrients. Such unhealthy lifestyle choices lead inevitably to weight gain and declining health.

脂肪に富む肉

栄養分（素）のない

　　It goes without saying that regular exercise is necessary to help you deal with the rigors of daily life. A simple step-by-step exercise regimen can make a huge difference to your level of health. Exercise boosts the body's metabolism, making you stronger, more energetic, and refreshed. As a result, your work and daily activities become easier to manage.

日常生活の厳しさ

運動法

代謝

　　Exercise is good not only for the young and healthy, but also for the elderly and for people with health problems or disabilities.❶ In fact, some disabled people are amazing athletes. In addition to regular exercise, however, a lifestyle that includes healthy habits such as eating the right foods and avoiding cigarettes and alcohol is essential.

運動選手

Notes

❶disability　障害：日本語の「障害」という言葉を問題視して「障がい」あるいは「障碍」を選ぶ人もいるが，日本リハビリテーション医学会では「障害」を用いている。

EXERCISES

1. 不要なアルファベットを除き，英単語を見つけなさい。

nodisabilityemexercisewihealthycometabolismsanutrient

1 __________ 2 __________ 3 __________ 4 __________ 5 __________

2. 英文の内容に合う適切な英語を（　　　）に書き入れなさい。

(1) A lack of exercise causes health (　　　　).

(2) (　　　　) food, (　　　　) meats, and rich (　　　　) snacks are loaded with calories but lacking in nutrients.

(3) Exercise makes you (　　　　), more (　　　　), and (　　　　).

3. 内容が正しい文にはTを，間違っている文にはFを記入しなさい。

(1) _____ Nowadays, people tend to walk more than drive.

(2) _____Typical diets these days are low in calories, but rich in nutrients.

(3) _____ The body's metabolism is boosted by exercise.

(4) _____ Exercise is not good for older people or for those with disabilities.

(5) _____ Healthy habits include having a good diet and avoiding alcohol and cigarettes.

Overview of the Body 身体の常識

The human body consists of many different parts — the heart, lungs, brain, stomach, kidneys, bones, muscles, and skin, among other organs. Do you know what each organ does? Here are some examples.

筋肉

The heart, an organ as big as your fist, pumps about 4.7 liters of blood throughout the body every minute! Blood flows from the heart through the arteries and returns to the heart through the veins. The blood❶ carries oxygen and nutrients to every part of your body.

動脈
静脈

The cone-shaped lungs are where air flows in and out of the body through air tubes. The lungs contain millions of ❷ tiny alveoli, each surrounded by very thin-walled capillaries where oxygen and carbon dioxide exchange takes place.

円錐形の
肺胞／毛細血管

The stomach breaks down the food you eat, and the small intestine❸ absorbs the nutrients in the food and so that the body can use them as fuel. The large intestine only absorbs water.

The bones support the body and protect important vital organs, such as the heart and lungs. The skull protects the very delicate brain. The skull may be likened to a container holding bean curd in water.

生命維持器官
豆腐

Many different muscles are attached to bones via tendons and ligaments to allow the body to move. Muscles perform two important functions: maintaining posture and generating body heat.

腱
靭帯
姿勢

The skin helps regulate the body's temperature. It is also very sensitive to many kinds of stimuli, thus protecting us from external hazards.

刺激《複》
危険

These and many other organs work together to keep us alive and help us stay healthy.

Notes

❶**blood**　血液の流れは，heart → aorta（大動脈）→ arteries（動脈）→ capillaries（毛細血管）→ veins（静脈）→ superior vena cava, inferior vena cava（上，下大静脈）→ heart

❷**millions of　何百万もの**：数の単位+sは「〜もの」となる。

❸**intestine**　腸の区分は，small intestine（小腸：duodenum十二指腸，jejunum空腸，ileum回腸）と large intestine（大腸：cecum 盲腸，colon 結腸，rectum 直腸）である。小腸は直径が大腸より短いので小(small)といわれるが，長さは6〜7 m，直径3〜4 cmあり，大腸はそれぞれ1.5 m，5〜8 cmである。小腸には無数の絨毛(villi)があり，食物の消化と吸収を，大腸は無絨毛で主として水分の吸収を行う。

EXERCISES

1. 日本語に相当する英語を書きなさい。

（1）脳 ______________　（2）胃 ______________　（3）腎臓 ______________

（4）肺 ______________　（5）筋肉 ______________

2. 英文の内容に合う適切な英語を（　　　　）に書き入れなさい。

（1）Blood flows from the heart through the（　　　　）to every part of the body and returns to the heart through the（　　　　）.

（2）The numerous（　　　　）in the lungs surrounded by very thin-walled capillaries.

（3）Food is broken down into smaller substances in the stomach and moves into the small（　　　　）.

（4）Vital organs like the heart and（　　　　）are supported and protected by bones.

（5）Muscles are attached to bones via（　　　　）and（　　　　）, thus allowing our body to move.

3. 内容が正しい文にはTを，間違っている文にはFを記入しなさい。

（1）_____ Oxygen and carbon dioxide exchange takes place in the heart.

（2）_____ The skull protects delicate several vital organs.

（3）_____ Without muscles, it would be impossible for us to move.

（4）_____ Muscles produce body heat.

（5）_____ The skin not only helps to regulate body temperature but also defends the body from external hazards.

Exercise Programs 運動計画

While you are exercising, many changes take place in your body. For example, your breathing❶ speeds up and the lungs take in more air to provide the body with more oxygen, your heart pumps blood faster to bring much needed oxygen and nutrients to the muscles, and you sweat to lower your rising body temperature. These increased demands on the body processes make each organ stronger and healthier.

呼吸

If you want to make your muscles bigger and stronger, exercises such as jogging or walking are not sufficient: harder exercise like sprinting for short periods is also required. However, it is important to keep in mind that pushing your body too hard can backfire. Excessive exercise puts a strain on the cardiovascular system❷ (the heart and blood vessels), the bones, muscles, and other organs. To prevent health problems, exercise sessions should include the three following elements:

逆効果である

心血管系（循環系）

(1) Warm-up

準備運動（ウォーミングアップ）

A proper warm-up gets the blood flowing and raises the temperature of the muscles. Once you start to sweat, you are ready for the next stage.

(2) Main exercise

What type of exercise you do and how long you do it for will depend on your preference and your physical condition. Walking, jogging, running, cycling, swimming, and skiing are among the most popular exercises you can do on your own. Generally speaking, exercise periods lasting 30 minutes or more are the most beneficial, but for beginners, training sessions limited to 20 minutes are advised.

トレーニングセッション

(3) Cooling down

整理運動（クールダウン）

After exercising, you need to cool down to give your heart and lungs time to return to normal functioning. If you finish your exercise session suddenly, extra blood will keep flowing to your muscles, because your heart will continue to pump blood to them at an accelerated rate. As a result, your other organs will not receive a sufficient supply of blood. A 5- or 10-minute cooling down period is needed to help the body gradually return to its normal resting state.

Notes

❶ **breathing**：動詞 breathe [brí:ð] の動名詞。ea の部分の発音が名詞は breath [brέθ]。

❷ **cardiovascular system**：心臓と血管からなる。
cardio- はギリシャ語 kardia 心臓に由来。vas- はラテン語 vas 脈管に由来。

EXERCISES

1. 適切な英語を（　　）に入れて文を完成させなさい。

(1) While you are exercising. . .

1) your (　　　　　) speeds up.

2) your (　　　　　) pumps faster.

3) your body (　　　　　) rises.

(2) If you want to make your (　　　　　) bigger and stronger, you have to do some strenuous exercise like, for example, running at full speed for short periods of time.

(3) (　　　　　) helps lower your body temperature.

2. 誤りのある箇所に下線を引き正しい語を書きなさい。

(1) If you want to increase muscle mass, jogging or walking is sufficient. (　　　　　)

(2) You need to allow at least 20 minutes to cool down after exercising. (　　　　　)

(3) If you end your exercise session suddenly, extra blood will stop flowing to your muscles. (　　　　　)

CHAPTER I

What is Rehabilitation?

CHAPTER I

What is Rehabilitation?
リハビリテーションとは

リハビリテーションという言葉が医学・医療の分野はもちろん，社会的にも定着したのは20世紀後半である。リハビリテーション医学はその先進国であるアメリカで，2つの大戦で負傷した多くの兵士たちを訓練によって社会復帰させることが大きな原動力になったと言えるが，日本では，整形外科学での小児麻痺の治療において形成されてきた。しかし，特に最近，「障害のある人の人間としての権利」「障害は個性である」「障害のある人の自立した生活」というような人権意識の高まりとともに，障害のある人の障害を軽減すると同時に，新たに健康な側面と能力を見出して，それを増進し，生命と生活と人生の質を高めることがリハビリテーションの最終目標とされるようになってきた。

ここではまずリハビリテーションの歴史とWHOの定義，関連分野の説明等によってその概念を把握する。

History of Rehabilitation　リハビリテーションの歴史

It is difficult to talk about the history of rehabilitation because the term has a wide range of meaning and is used differently in different settings. The Latin from which the word is derived "to make fit again". In health care, rehabilitation provides interventions that go beyond medical treatment to help those with injuries and illnesses to re-establish themselves as productive and socially integrated citizens.

While the idea has been around for centuries, it only began to take hold during the First World War, when millions of injured soldiers had a clear need of rehabilitation on their return home. Between the wars, the concept of rehab struggled for recognition, perhaps because people thought there would never again be that type of need: another war was unthinkable. But of course the Second World War came along, and the need again became apparent.

Sometime after the Second World War, the specialty of rehabilitation became formalized in North America. Writing

Latin: ラテン語
interventions: 介入
injuries: 損傷，傷害，外傷
rehab: ＝rehabilitation《主に米》

in 1958, Dr. Howard Rusk*, one of the early promoters of rehabilitation in the US, stated that its objectives were to eliminate the physical disability if possible; to alleviate the disability to the greatest extent possible; and to retrain the person with a residual physical disability to live and work to the hilt of their capabilities.

除去する／身体障害／軽減させる

To meet these objectives, a "Rehab Team" was required. The most commonly included members of that team were physicians, occupational therapists (OTs), physical therapists (PTs), and speech and language therapists (STs) or speech-language pathologists (SLPs). Often the doctors were specialists in physical medicine, also known as physiatrists. The players on the team would vary with the settings: in-patient rehab would also have nurses, and out-patient rehab might include social workers and vocational specialists. But if we focus just on the team of OT, PT, ST, SLP, and physiatrist, then we know that each of those disciplines also has a broader focus that operates outside of the rehab team. So you could say that rehab is more than the sum of its parts and, at the same time, that it is less than the entity that is each of its parts.

作業療法士／理学療法士

言語聴覚士

リハビリテーション医

入院患者〔の〕

外来患者〔の〕

(Reproduced with permission from Rehabilitation Sciences Sector, University of Toronto)

［*］ Dr. Howard Rusk (1901～1989)：アメリカにおけるリハビリテーション医学・治療の先駆者，推進者。ADL (日常生活動作) という概念を医学のなかに明確に位置づけた。ニューヨーク大学医師。

ことばのルーツ

rehabilitation　リハビリテーション，社会復帰

語源はラテン語のre-(再び)＋habilitare(能力を与える，資格を与える)である。habilitareは動詞habilitas(持つ，ある状態に保つ)から派生した名詞habilitas(能力)に由来する。16世紀はじめごろの英語辞書には「長期間，病床あるいは牢獄にいた人を再び有用な生活を送れるように援助すること」とある。20世紀になって，大戦で負傷した人びとを社会復帰できるように訓練，援助が広がった。現在，保健医療・福祉分野では，機能障害を回復して社会に復帰する能力を与える，という意味で用いられる。

Four major fields of rehabilitation
リハビリテーションの領域

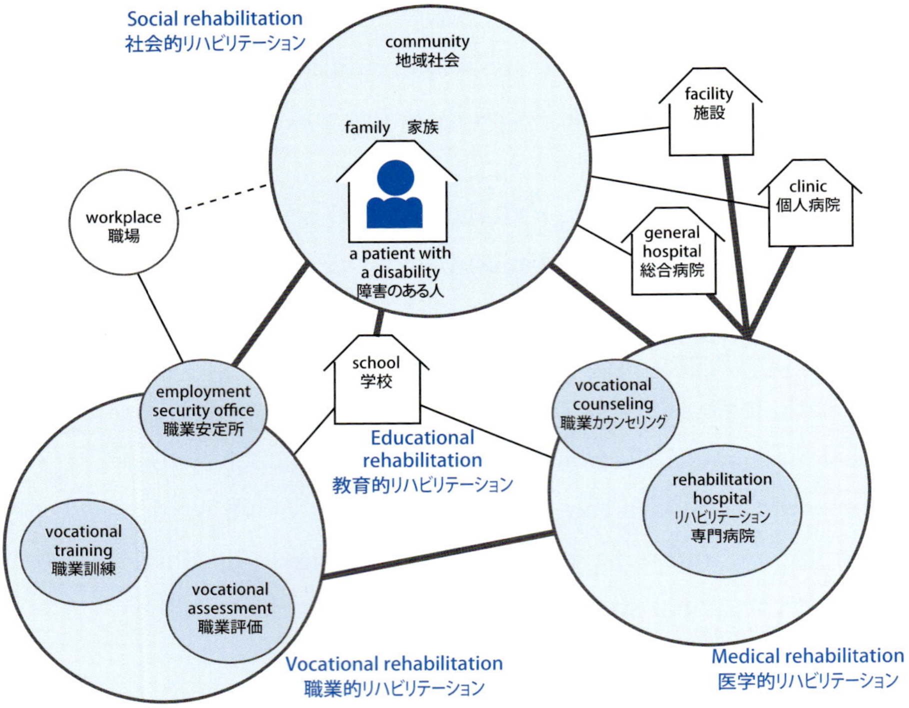
Social rehabilitation
社会的リハビリテーション
community
地域社会
family 家族
a patient with
a disability
障害のある人
facility
施設
clinic
個人病院
general
hospital
総合病院
workplace
職場
school
学校
employment
security office
職業安定所
Educational
rehabilitation
教育的リハビリテーション
vocational
counseling
職業カウンセリング
rehabilitation
hospital
リハビリテーション
専門病院
vocational
training
職業訓練
vocational
assessment
職業評価
Vocational rehabilitation
職業的リハビリテーション
Medical rehabilitation
医学的リハビリテーション

Professionals in rehabilitation services
リハビリテーションの専門家

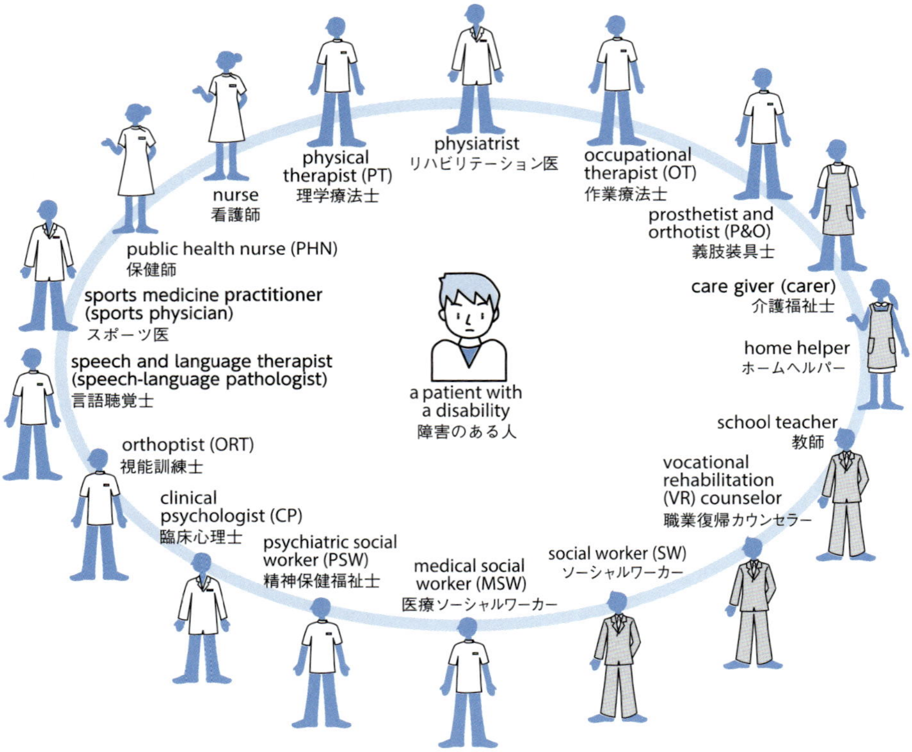
physical
therapist (PT)
理学療法士
physiatrist
リハビリテーション医
occupational
therapist (OT)
作業療法士
nurse
看護師
prosthetist and
orthotist (P&O)
義肢装具士
public health nurse (PHN)
保健師
sports medicine practitioner
(sports physician)
スポーツ医
care giver (carer)
介護福祉士
home helper
ホームヘルパー
speech and language therapist
(speech-language pathologist)
言語聴覚士
a patient with
a disability
障害のある人
school teacher
教師
orthoptist (ORT)
視能訓練士
vocational
rehabilitation
(VR) counselor
職業復帰カウンセラー
clinical
psychologist (CP)
臨床心理士
psychiatric social
worker (PSW)
精神保健福祉士
medical social
worker (MSW)
医療ソーシャルワーカー
social worker (SW)
ソーシャルワーカー

EXERCISES

1. （　　）の中の文字を正しい順序にしなさい。

(1) re (a a b h i i l t) tion (　　　　　　　　　　)
(2) pro (e f i n o s s) (　　　　　　　　　　)
(3) t (a e h i p r s t) (　　　　　　　　　　)

2. 英語に相当する日本語を選びなさい。

(1) cardiac rehabilitation (　　)
(2) social rehabilitation (　　)
(3) home rehabilitation (　　)
(4) vocational rehabilitation (　　)
(5) medical rehabilitation (　　)

a. 社会的リハビリテーション
b. 医学的リハビリテーション
c. 職業的リハビリテーション
d. 心臓リハビリテーション
e. 呼吸リハビリテーション
f. 在宅リハビリテーション

3. リハビリテーションに関連する職種を，できるだけ多く書きなさい。

4. 英文の内容に合うように，（　　）の英語のいずれかを選択しなさい。

(1) The modern concept of rehabilitation took root during World War I to meet the needs of the numerous (wounded/rehabilitated) soldiers returning home from war.
(2) Rehabilitation didn't become a formal specialty in the US until after (World War I / World War II).
(3) To meet the objectives of rehabilitation listed by Dr. Howard Rusk, it was necessary to create teams of specialists in (various fields/one field).

Physical Therapy and Physical Therapists
理学療法と理学療法士

Physical therapy, also known as physiotherapy, is one of the many health care professions. It involves the use of various physical stimuli to treat a variety of medical conditions. Ultraviolet light, sunlight, electric heating pads, cold packs, and paraffin baths, for example, are all used in physical therapy, along with many other stimuli and devices.

Physical therapy is useful in treating such conditions as heart and lung diseases, paralysis, strokes, and muscle weakness, and also in helping patients with physical impairments❶ caused by fractures, injuries, amputations, and other orthopedic conditions. For patients with such impairments, physical therapists (or physiotherapists) use various kinds of equipment and self-help devices to relieve pain and to restore the greatest possible mobility and functional ability. Weights, dumbbells, parallel bars, stationary bicycles, and pulleys are good for building muscle strength, and patients are aided in carrying out their daily activities by such devices such as crutches, splints, braces, and wheelchairs.

Physical therapists also cooperate with physiatrists, occupational therapists, speech therapists, and other professionals to improve patients' quality of life. They work not only in hospitals but also in outpatient clinics, inpatient rehabilitation facilities, nursing homes, hospices, schools, industrial workplaces, fitness centers, and sports training facilities.

紫外線／冷湿布

麻痺／脳卒中／筋力低下

骨折／切断

整形外科的

自助具

〔訓練用〕固定式自転車

松葉杖／副子, 副木, スプリント／装具／車椅子

生活の質

介護施設

Notes

❶ **impairment** とは，たとえば片麻痺や下肢切断など，生物レベルでの障害をいう。
disability は書字不能や歩行障害など，impairmentによって生じる能力面の障害であり，リハビリテーションや心のもち方で状態が改善される。
handicap とは，障害が社会生活においてどの程度不利であるかを問題にする。国際障害分類（ICIDH-2）は2001年に「国際生活機能分類（ICF）」に改訂され，impairmentはそのままに，disabilityはactivity limitation（活動の制限）に，handicapはparticipation restriction（参加の制限）に変更された。

Occupational Therapy and Occupational Therapists
作業療法と作業療法士

Occupational therapy is aimed at helping people with illnesses, injuries, or disabilities improve their ability to perform everyday tasks in their homes, communities and workplaces. Occupational therapists (OTs) provide important and meaningful interventions for children with disabilities to help them take part in school activities, for people with injuries or illnesses to assist them in regaining physical strength and mental health, and for older people to support them through the physical and cognitive changes they undergo.

OTs focus on helping people with disabilities not only to improve their basic motor functions and reasoning abilities, but also to find ways to compensate for permanent loss of function in their routine work. OTs plan tailor-made programs for individuals, and work together with other rehabilitation staff under the guidance of a physiatrist. Their work mainly involves the following four activities:

1. building up patients' muscle strength and ability to move their joints in daily activities like handling chopsticks and cooking;
2. training patients in comparatively complex activities, such as reading and recreational activities, to resolve higher-order brain dysfunction, which makes it difficult for patients to

interventions：介入
cognitive changes：認知的変化
compensate for：補償する，埋め合わせる
routine work：日課
higher-order brain dysfunction：高次脳（機能）障害

understand time, grasp the situations they find themselves in, and carry out the routines of daily life;

3. improving patients' skills in activities of daily living (ADL), such as eating, changing clothes, personal hygiene, toileting, knitting, gardening, cooking, taking photos, and so forth;
4. having patients engage in role-playing activities to help them acquire the social skills necessary to settle problems, learn effectively, and maintain personal relations in their communities.

日常生活動作

お菓子作り

OTs work in a wide variety of settings, such as hospitals, rehabilitation facilities, day-care centers, outpatient clinics, nursing homes, schools, child welfare institutions, facilities for children with mental retardation, day-care centers, long-term care health facilities, etc. Because it helps individuals have independent, productive, and satisfying lives, occupational therapy is a rewarding career.

(外来) 診療所

児童福祉施設／知的障害児童施設

介護老人福祉施設

Speech and Language Therapy and Speech and Language Therapists
言語聴覚療法と言語聴覚士

Speech and language therapy is the treatment of speech and language-related conditions and disorders. It is targeted at 3 main groups: (1) children who are developmentally speech and/or hearing impaired; (2) people who have difficulty in swallowing and/or who have experienced accidental ingestion into their lungs; and (3) people suffering from diseases affecting language ability.

発達的に

嚥下

誤嚥

言語能力

Speech and language therapists are trained to evaluate, diagnose, and treat speech and language disorders. In children, the most common disorders are:

判断する

birth defects: cleft palate, cleft lip

language delay

出生時欠損／口蓋裂／口唇裂

言語〔発達〕遅滞

difficulties in producing specific sounds
hearing impairment 聴覚障害（難聴）
stammering (or stuttering) 吃（きつ）
learning disabilities (or disorders) 学習障害
autism or social interaction difficulties 自閉症

In adults, speech and language therapists are typically involved in treating speech and language disorders resulting from:

hearing loss 難聴
stammering
cancers of the head, neck and throat
head injuries
neurological disorders, such as dementia, Alzheimer's disease, and Parkinson's disease 認知症
stroke 脳卒中
multiple sclerosis 多発〔性〕硬化〔症〕
mental health issues 精神衛生上の問題

Depending on the nature and severity of the disorder, common treatments range from physical strengthening exercises, instructive or repetitive practice and drilling, to the use of audio-visual aids or picture symbols. For example, exercises such as blowing a whistle or licking ice cream can strengthen the tongue and lips. Treatment of language disorders may involve word play activities, and games to activate word recovery, understanding or conversation.

性質と重症度
視聴覚教材
口笛を吹くこと

Speech and language therapists work in a variety of different settings, including schools, hospitals, outpatient clinics, rehabilitation centers, prisons, and clients' homes. They often coordinate with other professionals (doctors, physical therapists, occupational therapists, care workers, psychologists, nurses, teachers, and also family members) to ensure that essential information about the patient is shared appropriately.

EXERCISES

1. 英語に相当する日本語を選びなさい。

(1) accidental ingestion (　　)
(2) cleft palate (　　)
(3) cognitive (　　)
(4) self-help devices (　　)
(5) stroke (　　)

a. 脳卒中　b. 脳梗塞　c. 口蓋裂
d. 口蓋唇　e. 嚥下　f. 誤嚥
g. 機器　h. 自助具　i. 情緒的
j. 認知的

2. 誤りを見つけなさい。

(1) ocupational therapy ____________________
(2) inpairment ____________________
(3) palarysis ____________________
(4) stamering ____________________
(5) palaffin bath ____________________

3. 省略語のフルスペルを書きなさい。

(1) PT (　　　　　　　　　　)
(2) OT (　　　　　　　　　　)
(3) ST (　　　　　　　　　　)

4. 内容が正しい文にはTを，間違っている文にはFを記入しなさい。

(1) _____ PTs use many kinds of equipment to help their patients, but they never use self-help devices.

(2) _____ There are many areas of practice in occupational therapy and the distinctions among them are always clear.

(3) _____ A wide variety of strategies ranging from physical strengthening exercise to the use of audio-visual aids or picture symbols are used in speech therapy.

CHAPTER II

Fundamentals of the Human Body for Rehabilitation

CHAPTER II

Fundamentals of the Human Body for Rehabilitation
リハビリテーションのための人体の基礎知識

障害者の身体的，心理的，社会的能力のリハビリテーションにおいて，人体の知識は疾病の理解と回復のための訓練の基礎となる。本章では，解剖学的基準である人体の断面・方向，可動域，肢位などの英語を学習する。

Plane and Direction 断面と方向

人体を以下のように区分し，その断面と方向を解剖学的基準とする。

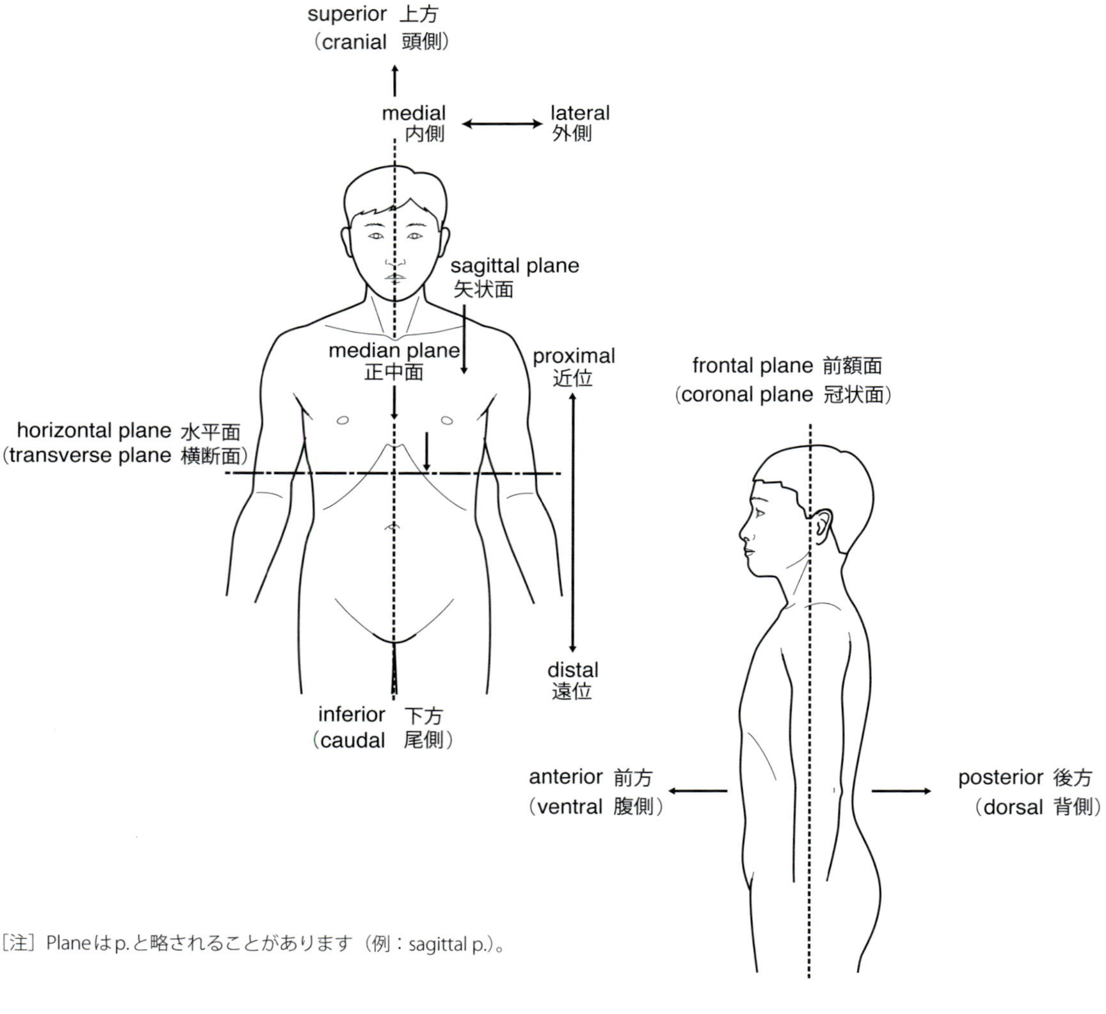

［注］Planeはp.と略されることがあります（例：sagittal p.）。

■ Plane　断面

①**median plane** 正中面：身体を垂直に左右2つに分割する断面。

②**sagittal plane** 矢状(しじょう)面：身体を正中面に対して平行に分けるすべての断面。

③**frontal plane** 前額面（**coronal plane**　冠状面）：身体を前後に垂直に分ける断面。

④**horizontal plane** 水平面（**transverse plane**　横断面）：身体を水平線に対して平行に横断する断面。

［注］sagittalのアクセントが第1音節にあることに注意。

■ Direction　方向

①**medial** 内側(ないそく)，**lateral** 外側(がいそく)：正中面に，“内側”はより近く，“外側”はより遠い。

②**superior** 上方（**cranial** 頭側），**inferior** 下方（**caudal** 尾側）：人体の特定の点から，“上方”は頭に近く，“下方”は足底に近い。

③**anterior** 前方（**ventral** 腹側），**posterior** 後方（**dorsal** 背側）：矢状面の方向に，“前方”は身体のより前，“後方”はより後ろ。

④**proximal** 近位，**distal** 遠位：体幹または起始に，“近位”はより近い，“遠位”はより遠い。

［注］起始（origin）とは，筋肉が骨に付着する2点のうち動かない方をいう。もう一方は停止（insertion）という。

■ Others　その他

①**superficial**　表在の

②**intermediate**　中間の

③**deep**　深在の

EXERCISES

1. 英語に相当する日本語を選びなさい。

(1) medial　　(　　)
(2) median plane　　(　　)
(3) sagittal plane　　(　　)
(4) distal　　(　　)
(5) lateral　　(　　)

a. 近位　b. 遠位　c. 内側　d. 外側　e. 正中面
f. 矢状面　g. 横断面　h. 冠状面

2. 同義語を選びなさい。

(1) anterior　　(　　)
(2) frontal　　(　　)
(3) inferior　　(　　)
(4) posterior　　(　　)
(5) transverse　　(　　)

a. caudal　b. coronal　c. dorsal　d. horizontal　e. ventral

Range of Motion (ROM) 関節可動域

ヒトは関節を動かすことで，身体の各部分を曲げる，伸ばす，挙げるなどの動作をする。関節を1点からほかの1点へ動かすことのできる範囲を関節可動域という。関節可動域運動は，関節拘縮（こうしゅく）（arthrogryposis: 関節包を含む関節包外の靱帯，筋，腱などの変化）によって関節運動が制限されることの改善，予防のために行われる。

Basic Terms of Movement 運動の基本用語

■ROMの基礎的表現

Angular Motion	角運動	Particular Motion	特定の運動
・flexion	屈曲	・flexion	屈曲
・extension	伸展	・extension	伸展
・abduction	外転	・varus	内反
・adduction	内転	・valgus	外反
・right rotation (rotation to the right)	右回旋	・inversion	内返し
・left rotation (rotation to the left)	左回旋	・eversion	外返し
・internal (medial) rotation	内旋	・dorsiflexion, dorsal flexion	背屈
・external (lateral) rotation	外旋	・plantar flexion	底屈
・pronation	回内	・palmar flexion	掌屈
・supination	回外	・side flexion（bending）	側屈
・elevation	挙上	・protrusion（protraction）	突出
・depression	下制	・retrusion（retraction）	後退
		・opposition	対立

［注］ab-は「～から」，ad-は「～へ」，in-は「～のなかへ」，ex-は「～の外へ」，op-は「～に反対方向に」，retr-は「後方へ」という意味の，方向を示す接頭辞。医学用語でよく用いられる。

Examples of Motions in the ROM 関節可動域における運動例

Cervix (Neck) 頸（首）

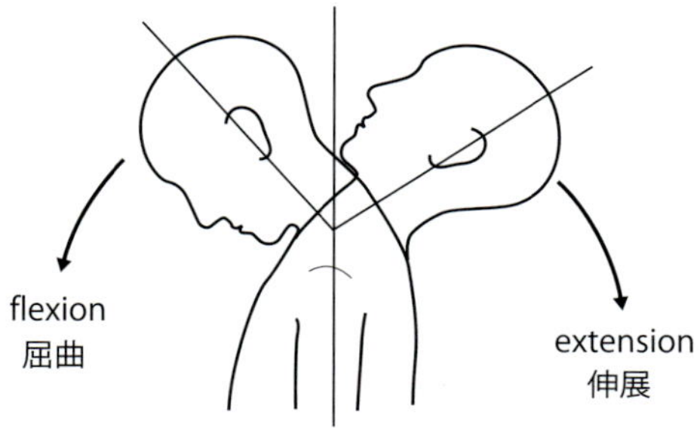

bending the neck forward/backward
首を前方/後方に曲げる

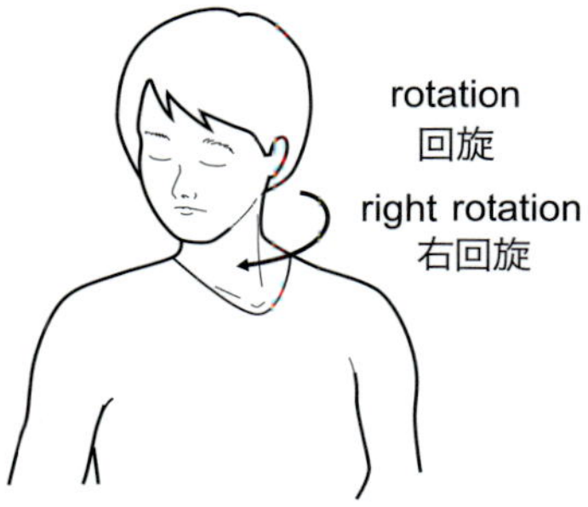

rotating the head and neck in a circle around a fixed point
頭と首を固定点の周囲で回転させる

Face 顔

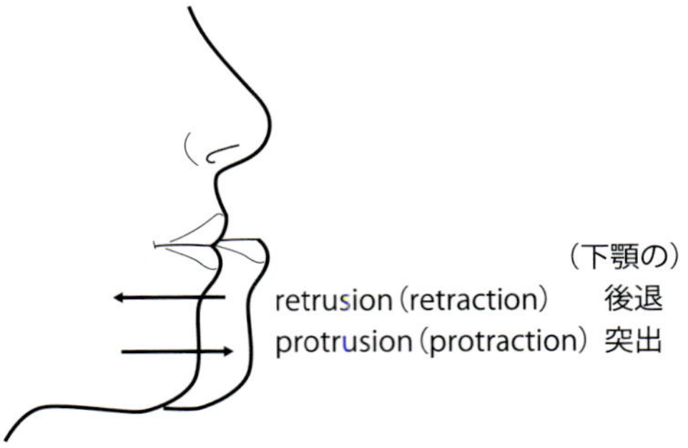

moving the lower jaw (= mandible) back/forth
下顎を後ろへ後退，あるいは前へ突出させる

Shoulder 肩

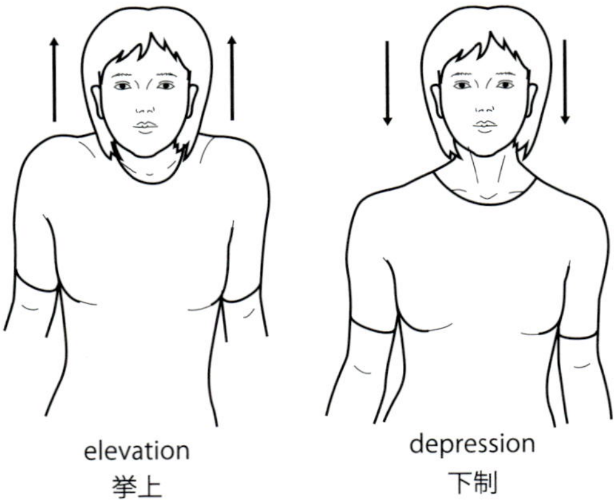

moving the shoulders up/down
肩を上げる / 下げる

Elbow 肘

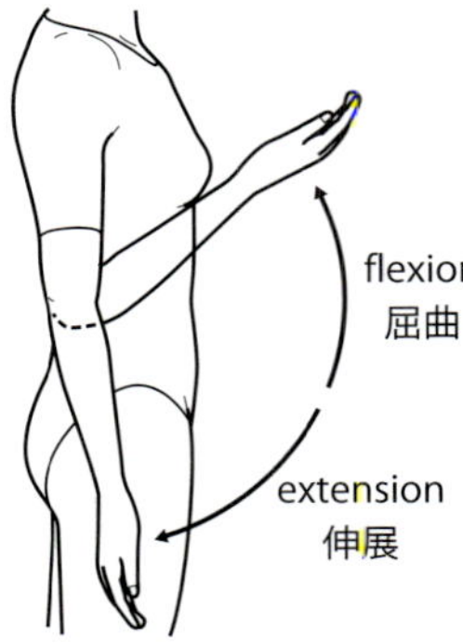

bending/straightening the arm at the elbow joint
腕を肘関節で曲げる / 伸ばす

Knee 膝

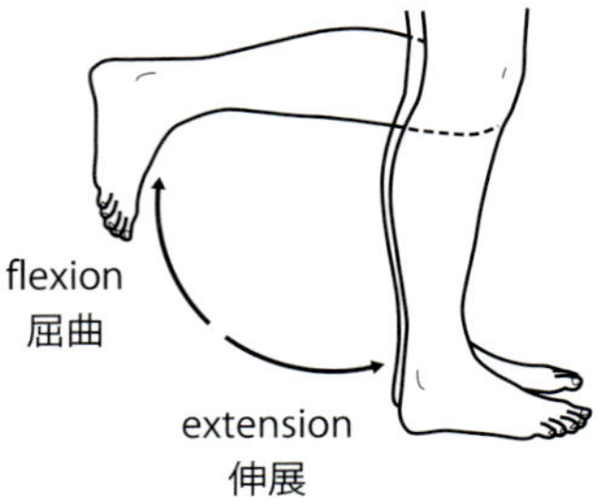

bending/straightening the lower leg at the knee joint
下肢を膝関節で曲げる / 伸ばす

Leg 脚

bending/straightening the leg at the hip joint
脚を股関節で曲げる / 伸ばす

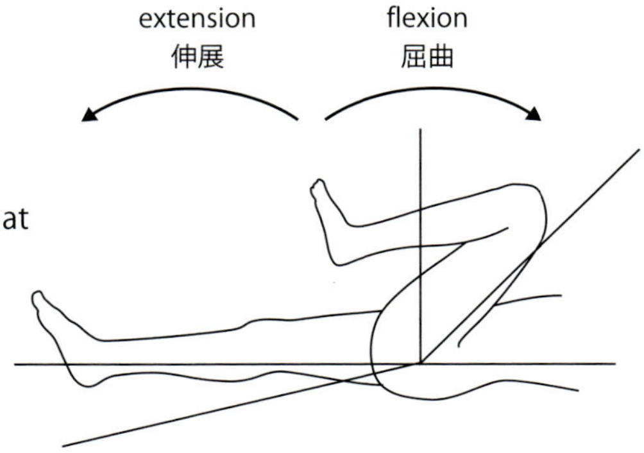

Hands and Fingers　手・手指

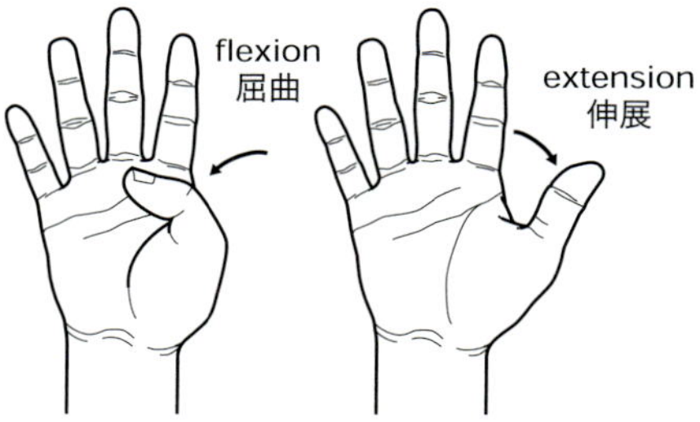

bending/extending the thumb
親指を曲げる/伸ばす

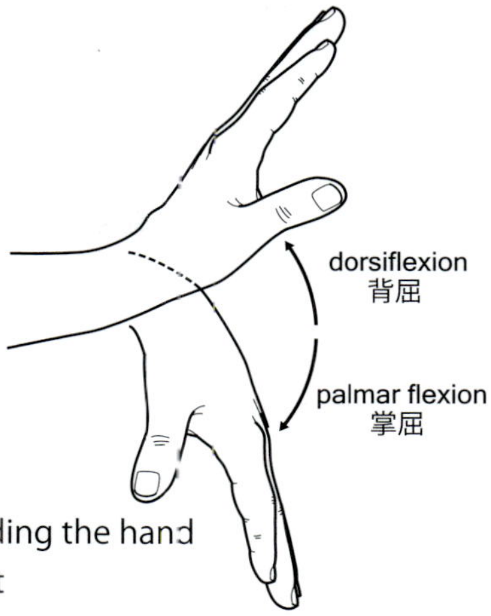

bending/extending the hand
at the wrist joint
手を手関節の位置で曲げる/伸ばす

holding out/bending the
fingers at the
metacarpophalangeal (MP)
and proximal interphalangeal
(PIP) joints
指を中手指節関節と指節間関節
の位置で曲げる/伸ばす

moving the forearm at the radial
and ulnar joints and turning the
hand upward/downward
前腕を橈・尺骨関節部で
動かし，手掌を上/下に
向ける

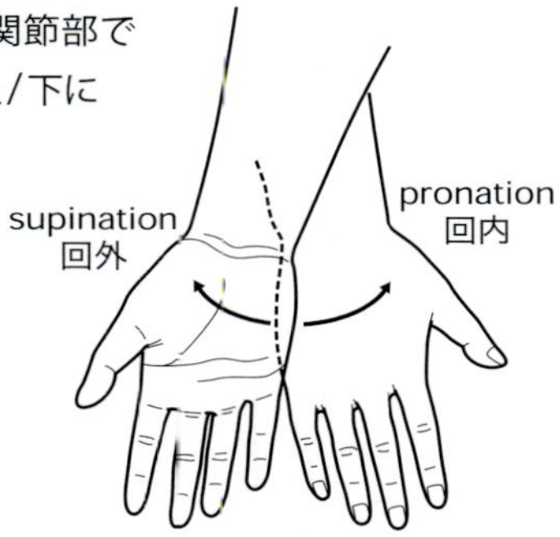

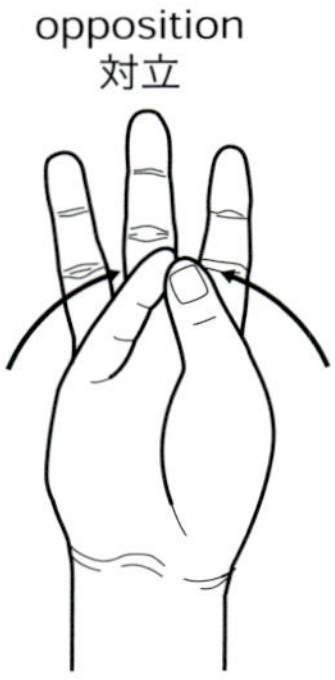

touching the thumb
with the little finger
親指を小指と向かい
合わせる

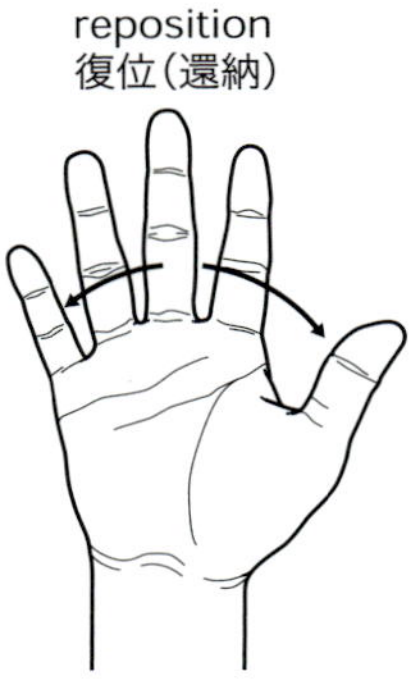

returning the thumb
and little finger
to their original
positions
親指と小指を元の
位置に戻す

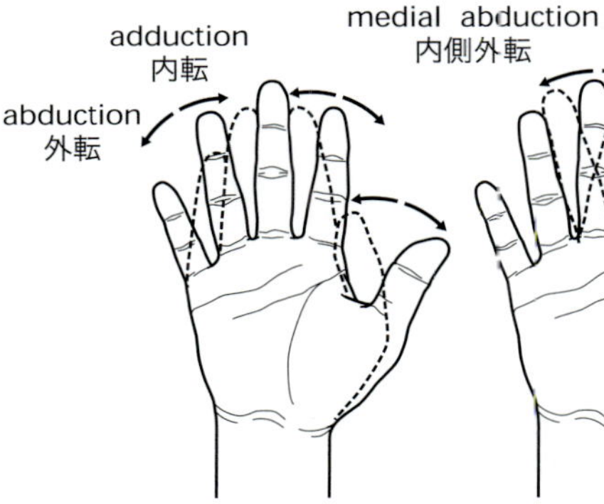

moving the 1st, 2nd,
4th and 5th fingers
toward the midline of
the hand
第1, 2, 4, 5指を手の
中線に向かって動かす

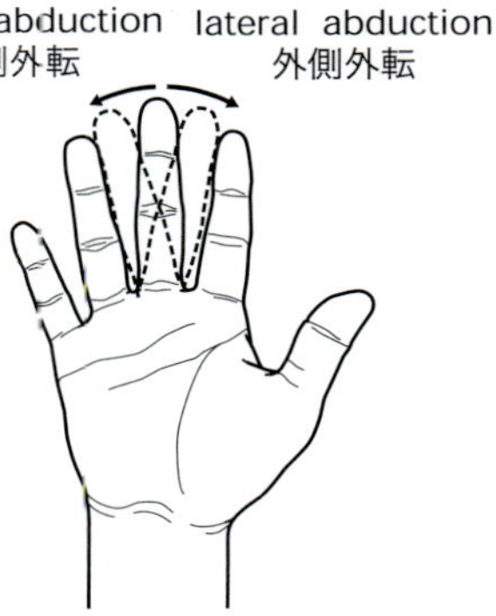

moving the 3rd
finger side to side
第3指を側方(左右)に
動かす

Foot 足

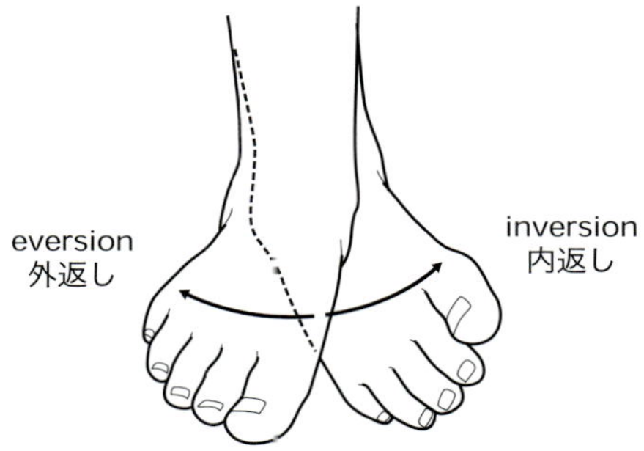

turning the foot inside/outside at the ankle joint
足を足関節の位置で内側/外側に回転する

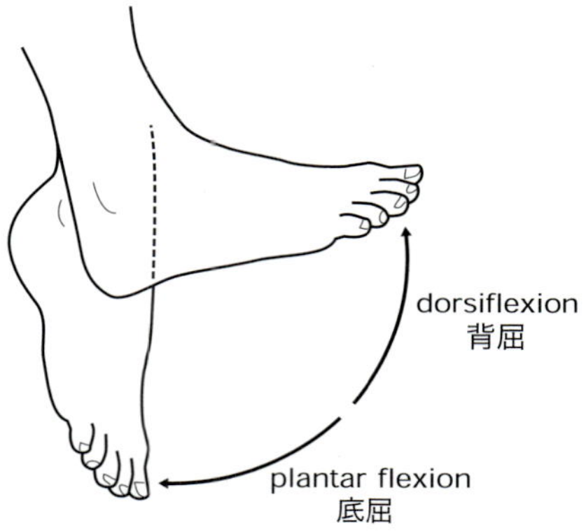

bending the foot or toes upward or to the sole of the foot at the ankle joint
足あるいは足趾を足関節の位置で上方/足底に向かって曲げる

Arms and Legs　腕・脚

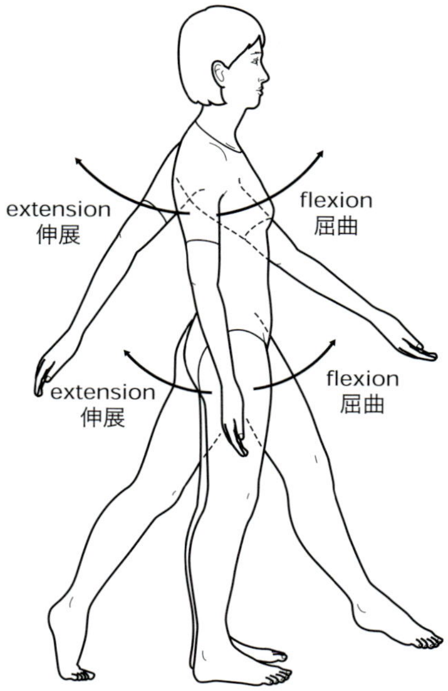

moving the arm forward/backward at the shoulder joint or the leg at the hip joint
腕を肩関節，脚を股関節の位置で前後に動かす

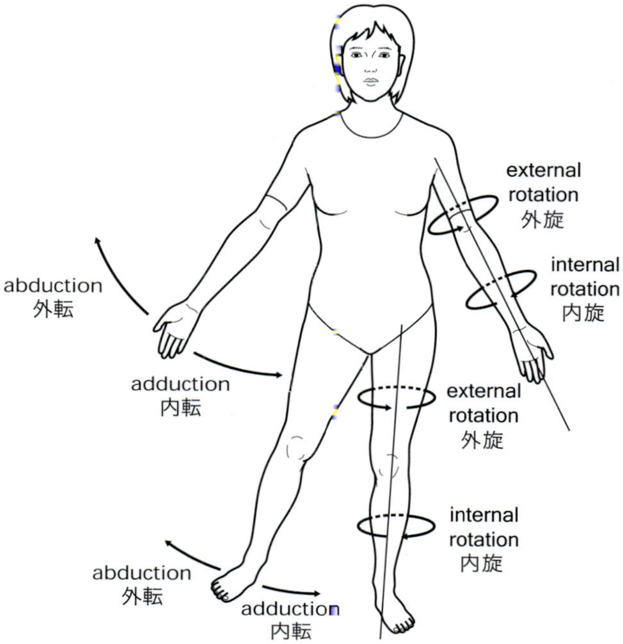

rotating the arm or leg in or out
腕または脚を外側/内側に回転する
（図の右側）

moving the arm or leg away from or toward the median plane
腕または脚を正中面から離す，あるいは近づける（図の左側）

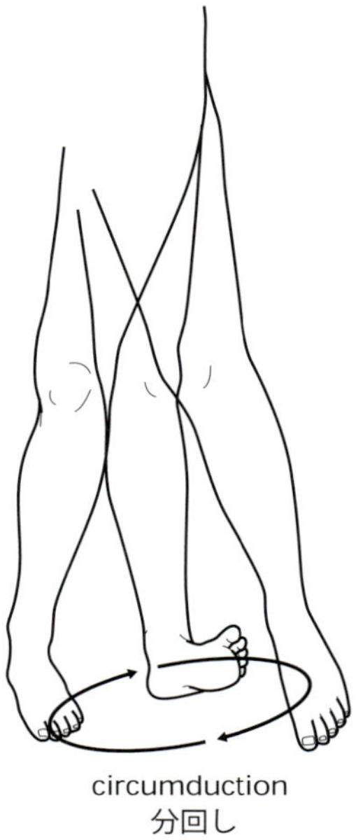

moving the arm or leg in a circle
手や足を回転させる

Body 身体

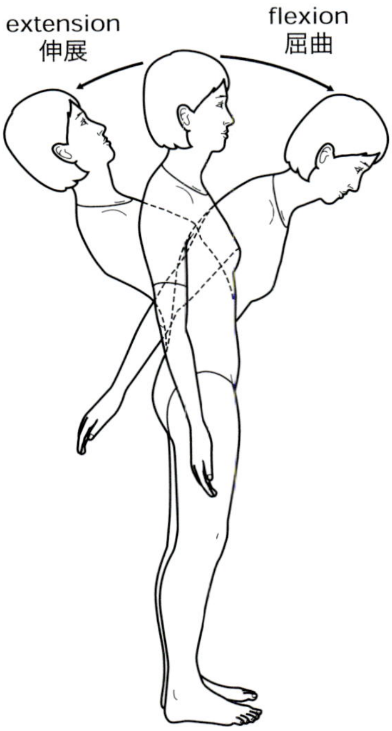

bending the upper half of the body forward/ backward at the intervertebral joints
上半身を前方/後方に椎間骨関節の位置で曲げる

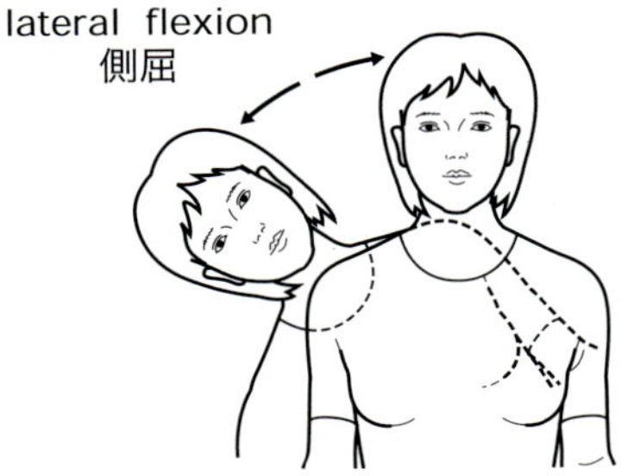

bending the upper trunk to the side
体幹を側方に曲げる

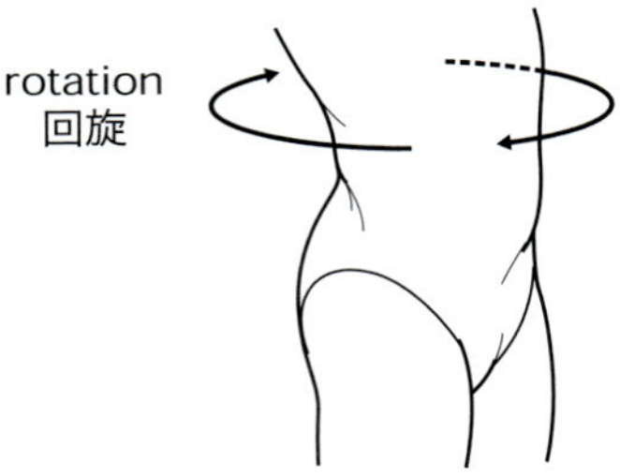

turning the upper trunk to the right and left at the waist
体幹を腰の位置で左右に回転する

■Decubitus Positions 臥位

supine position
背臥位

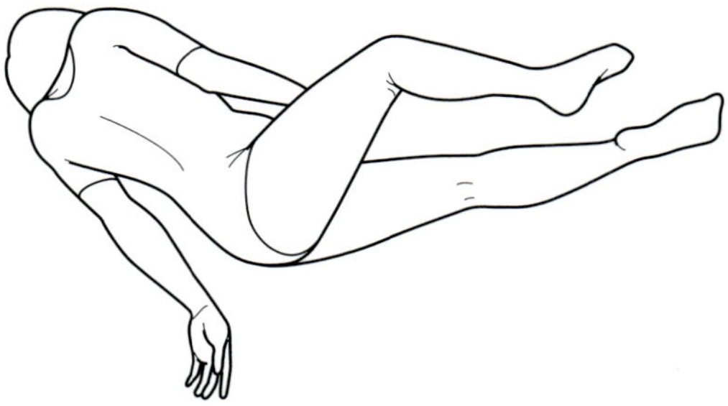

Sims' position (semiprone position)
シムス位（半腹臥位）

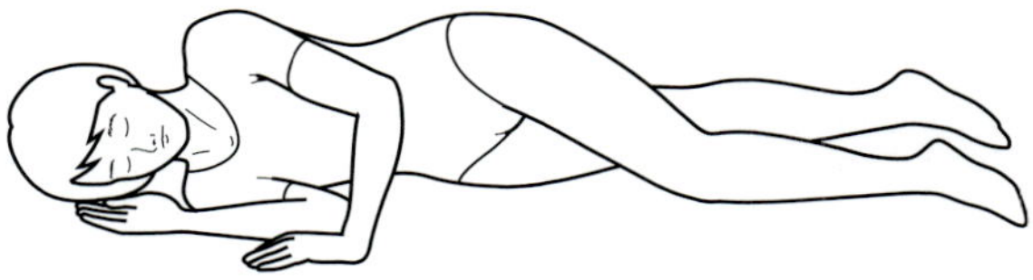

half side-lying position
半側臥位

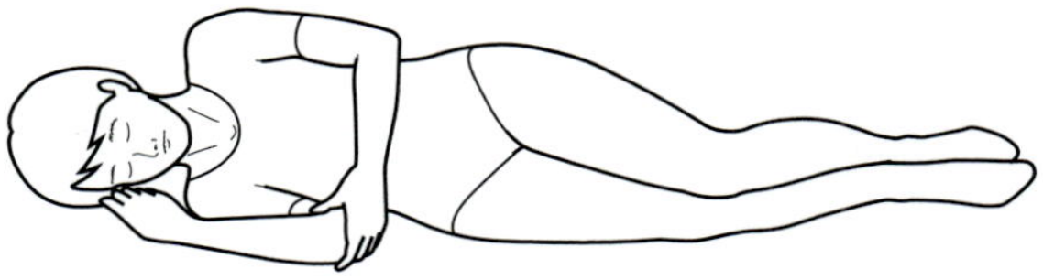

side-lying position
側臥位（横臥位）

prone position
腹臥位（伏臥位）

■ Standing Position 立位

front
正面

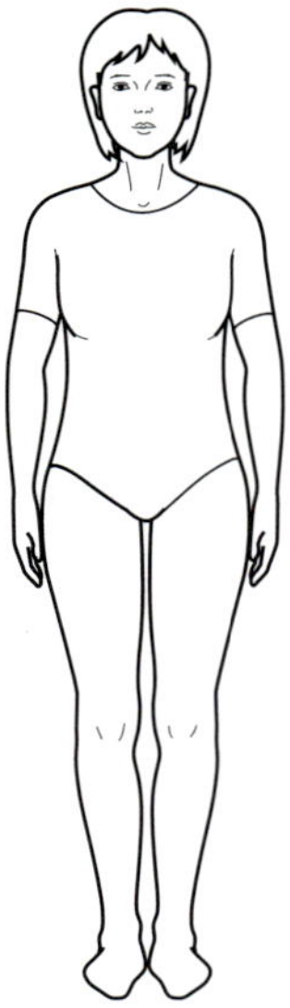

side
側面

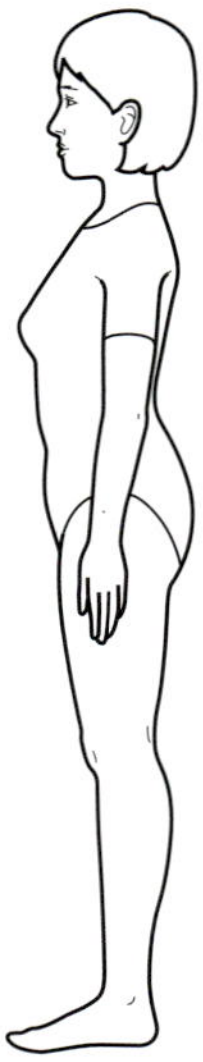

■ Sitting Positions 座位

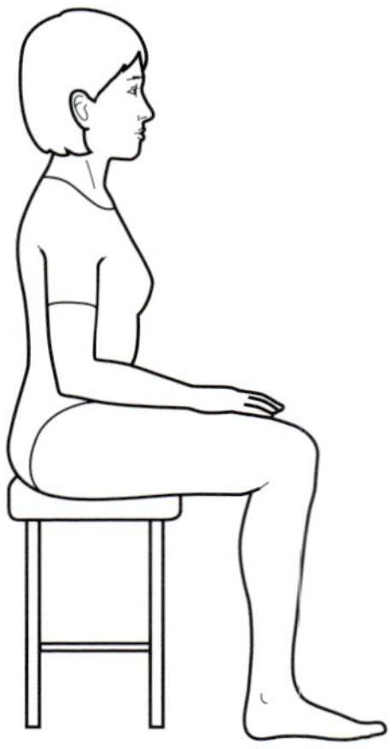

sitting position
椅座位

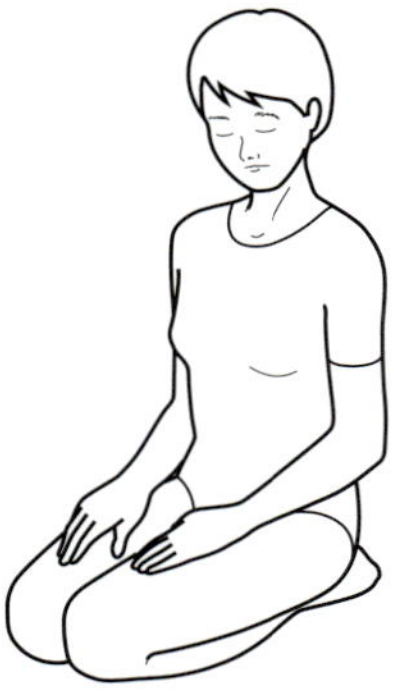

kneeling on the floor
正座

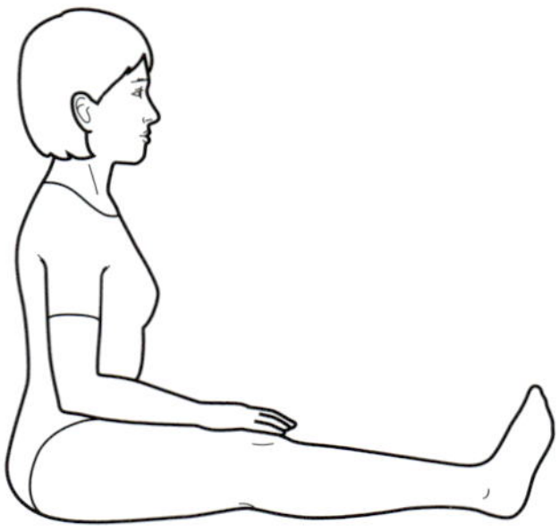

long sitting position
長座位

cross-legged sitting position
あぐら位

Fowler's position, half-lying position
ファウラー位（半臥位）

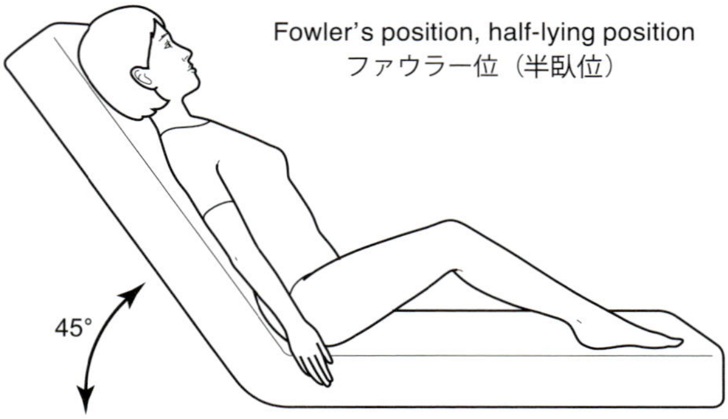

Major Joints and Regions of the Body 主要関節と部位

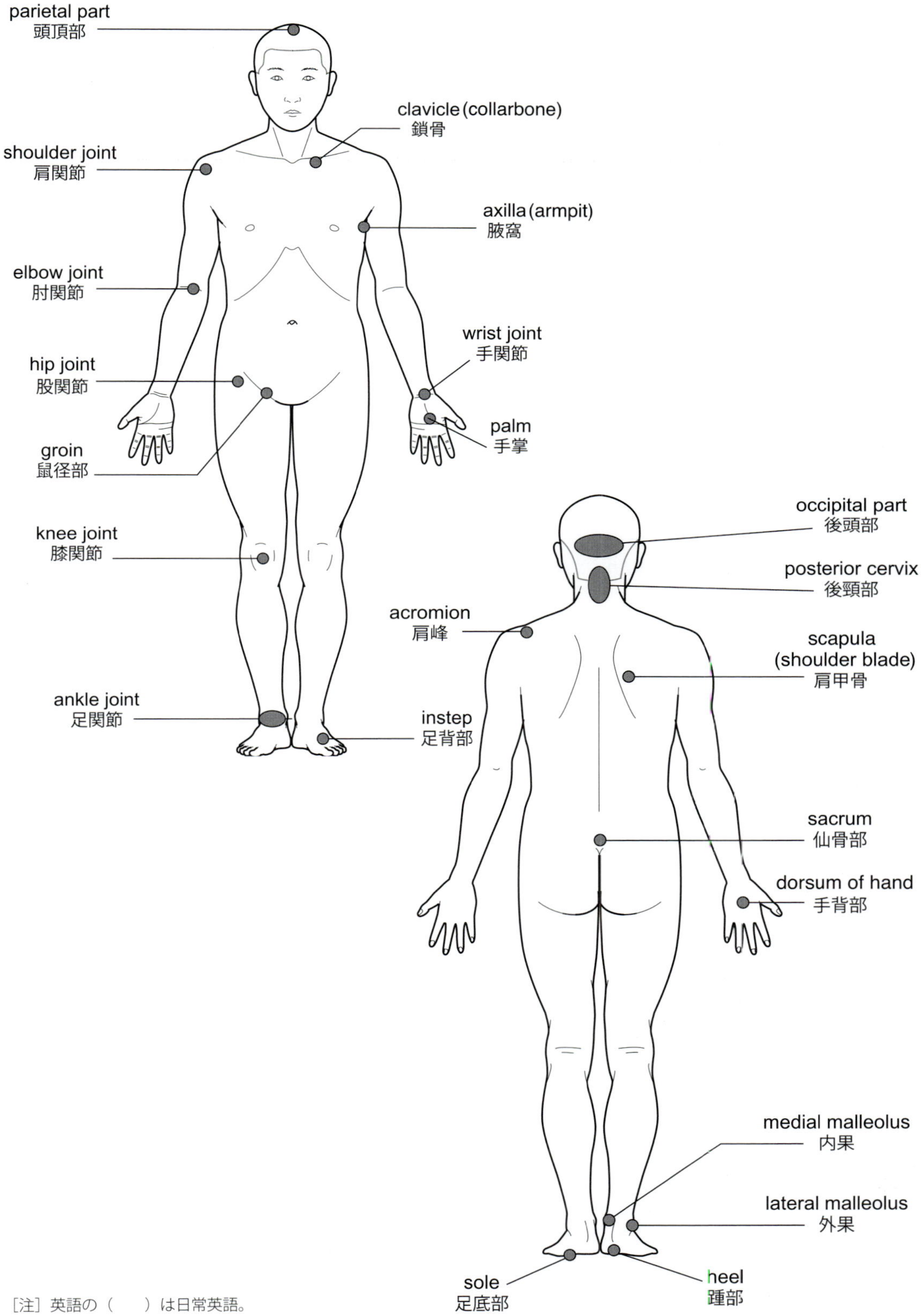

[注] 英語の（　　）は日常英語。

EXERCISES

1. (1)～(5)の英語に相当する日本語を記入し，その説明に該当するものをa～eから選びなさい。

(1) abduction ( ) ( )
(2) flexion ( ) ( )
(3) inversion ( ) ( )
(4) pronation ( ) ( )
(5) rotation ( ) ( )

a. Movement where part of the body moves away from the midline of the body or from a neighboring part
b. The action of bending or the condition of being bent
c. Turning part of the body toward the inside or being turned toward the inside
d. Turning the hand around so that the palm faces downwards
e. Movement in an arc around a fixed point

2. 英語に相当する日本語を選びなさい。

(1) cross-legged sitting position ( )
(2) long sitting positon ( )
(3) prone position ( )
(4) side-lying position ( )
(5) supine position ( )

a. 半背臥位　b. 背臥位　c. 腹臥位　d. 側臥位
e. 長座位　f. あぐら位　g. 正座

CHAPTER III

The Structure of the Human Body

CHAPTER III

The Structure of the Human Body
人体の構造

骨格系は多種の骨と，それらをつなぐ軟骨，腱，靱帯からなる。その働きは，①身体を形づくり体重を支える，②筋肉が付着し身体運動を可能にする，③脳，心臓，肺，脊髄，消化器，生殖器など，生命を維持し，知的活動を行い，生命を存続させる重要でしかも損傷を受けやすい繊細な器官を保護する，④骨髄で血液を産生することである。

骨格系を知ることは，障害をもつ人の社会復帰を目指すADL（activities of daily living: 日常生活動作）をはじめとした身体訓練のために必要である。

The Skeletal System 骨格系

BACKGROUND INFORMATION

The skeletal system of the human body consists of 206–210 bones, with the exact number of small bones in the hands and feet varying slightly from person to person. Bone is a dry, dense tissue composed of a calcium-phosphorus mineral (65%), together with organic matter and water (35%). Bone is covered with a living membrane called the periosteum, which contains bone-forming cells, or osteoblasts. During embryonic development, the skeletal framework is composed of cartilage and membranes.

稠密な組織／リン酸カルシウム類ミネラル

骨膜

骨芽細胞

軟骨

〔骨〕膜

(Reproduced with permission from "The Human Body" by Edward P. Ortleb and Richard Cardice. Milliken Publishing Company, 1986)

☆ これだけは覚えておきたい英語

- **the skeletal system** 骨格系
- **skeleton** 骨格
- **bone** 骨
- **tissue** 組織
- **cartilage** 軟骨
- **membrane** 膜

［注］skeletonのつづりに注意。以後，器官名に必要な定冠詞theは省略する場合がある。

Human Skeleton　骨格

人体の骨格は，200余りの骨と軟骨とともに連結し人体を支える。（　）は骨の数を示す。

Axial skeleton 軸骨格（80）

1.	**cranium (skull)**	**頭蓋（29）**
	neurocranium (brain case)	脳頭蓋（14）
	viscerocranium (facial bones)	内臓頭蓋（顔面骨）（14）
	hyoid bone (tongue bone)	舌骨（1）
2.	**thoracic cage**	**胸郭（25）**
	sternum	胸骨（1）
	rib	肋骨（24）
3.	**spine, vertebral column (backbone)**	**脊柱（26）**（p. 39参照）
	vertebra	椎骨（24）
	sacrum	仙骨（1）
	coccyx	尾骨（1）

Appendicular skeleton　付属肢骨格（126）

1.	**upper extremities (upper limbs)**	**上肢（64）**
	clavicle (collarbone)	鎖骨（2）
	scapula (shoulder blade)	肩甲骨（2）
	humerus (arm bone)	上腕骨（2）
	radius	橈骨（2）
	ulna	尺骨（2）
	carpal bones	手根骨（16）
	metacarpal bones	中手骨（10）
	phalanges of fingers	指骨（28）

2.	**lower extremities (lower limbs)**	**下肢（62）**
	ilium (hip bone)	寛骨（2）
	femur	大腿骨（2）
	patella	膝蓋骨（2）
	tibia	脛骨（2）
	fibula	腓骨（2）
	tarsal bones	足根骨（14）
	metatarsal bones	中足骨（10）
	phalanges	指骨（28）

［注］各骨の場所は次ページの図を参照。英語の（　）は日常英語。

ことばのルーツ

cranium と skull　頭蓋

craniumはギリシャ語のkranion，**skull**はスウェーデン語のskulleに由来する。脳を収容する箱の役割をするので，顔面骨を含まない。skeleton [skélətn] の語源は，skeleton soma（乾いた，ひからびた体）という意味のギリシャ語skeletosである。

① cranium; skull	頭蓋（とうがい）
② acromion	肩峰（けんぽう）
③ clavicle	鎖骨
④ scapula	肩甲骨
⑤ sternum	胸骨
⑥ rib	肋骨
⑦ floating rib	遊走肋骨
⑧ spine, vertebral column*	脊柱
⑨ ilium	腸骨
⑩ sacrum*	仙骨
⑪ coccyx*	尾骨
⑫ ischium	坐骨
⑬ pubis	恥骨
⑭ greater trochanter	大転子
⑮ femur	大腿骨
⑯ patella	膝蓋骨
⑰ tibia	脛骨
⑱ fibula	腓骨
⑲ tarsal bones	足根骨（そっこんこつ）
⑳ humerus	上腕骨
㉑ ulna	尺骨
㉒ radius	橈骨（とうこつ）
㉓ carpal bone	手根骨（しゅこんこつ）

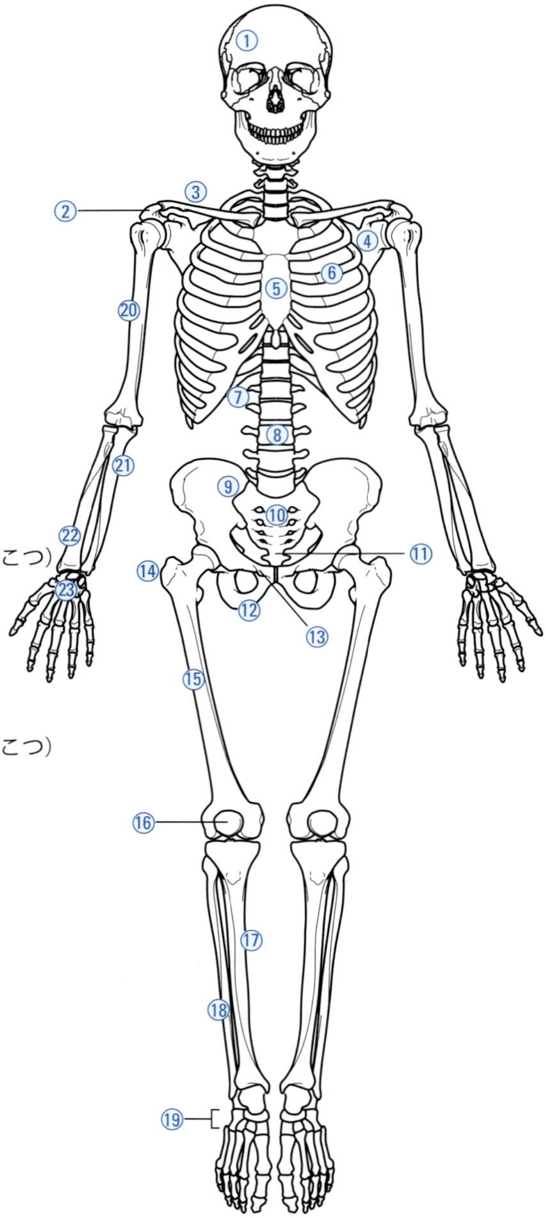

［注］＊印については，次ページ図参照。

Vertebral Column 脊柱

首の7椎は頸椎である。第一頸椎（環椎）は頭蓋骨を支える。次に胸部の背後にある12の胸椎が続き，脊柱下部に5つの腰椎がある。仙骨と尾骨は5つの腰椎と癒合した4つの尾椎で形成される。

①	cervical vertebrae	頸椎（7）
①-1	atlas	環椎（第一頸椎）
①-2	axis	軸椎（第二頸椎）
②	thoracic vertebrae	胸椎（12）
③	lumbar vertebrae	腰椎（5）
④	sacrum	仙骨（1）
	= sacral vertebrae	＝仙椎（5）
⑤	coccyx	尾骨（1）
	= coccygeal vertebrae	尾椎（3～5）
⑥	vertebra	椎骨
⑦	intervertebral disc	椎間板
⑧	intervertebral foramen	椎間孔
⑨	spinous process	棘突起

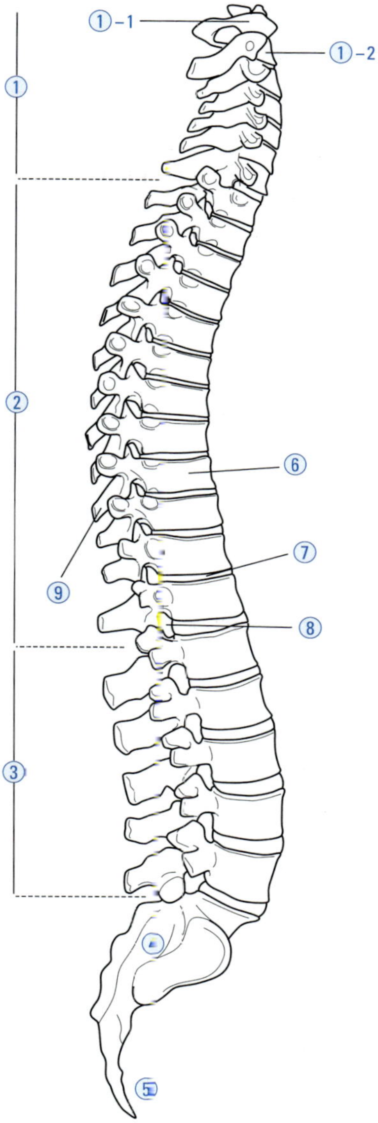

ことばのルーツ

atlas 環椎（第一頸椎）

第一頸椎の英語名**atlas**は，ギリシャ神話に登場する巨神Atlasが最高神ゼウスの怒りに触れて天空を肩にかつがされたことに由来する。the Atlantic Mountains（アトラス山脈），the Atlantic Ocean（大西洋）などは当時，そのあたりが地球の中心と考えられたことから。atlasは頭蓋の傾き運動をするだけである。第二頸椎の丈夫な歯突起が第一頸椎窩に入り込み，その間で靭帯が上下，横に支持しているので回転運動が可能となる。そのため第二頸椎はaxis（軸椎）とよばれる。

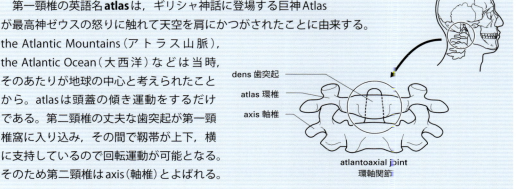

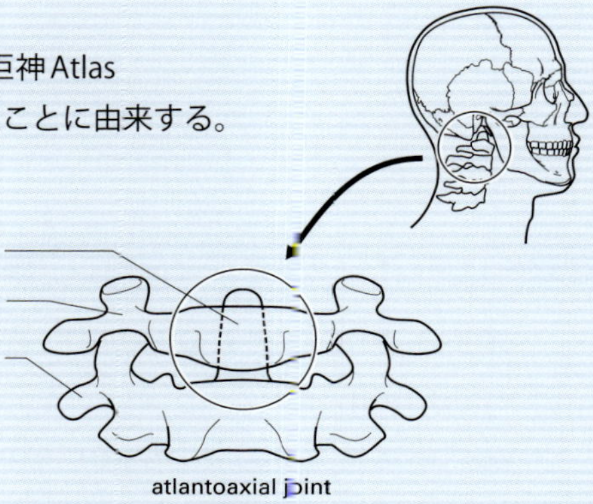

Bones　骨

骨は連続した組織の層(ハバース系)からなる固い外層(緻密質)と骨髄を含む柔らかい内部(海綿質)から形成される。

① periosteum	骨膜
② compact substance; compact bone	緻密質
③ spongy substance; cancellous bone	海綿質
④ medullary cavity	骨髄腔
⑤ articular cartilage	関節軟骨
⑥ epiphysis	骨端
⑦ diaphysis	骨幹
⑧ joint capsule	関節包

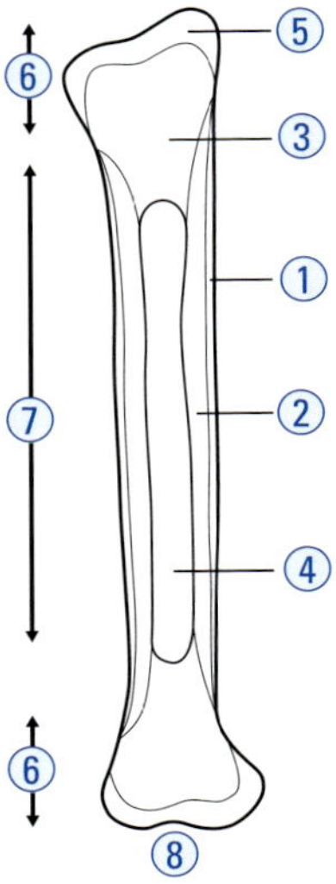

Classification of the bone 骨の外形による分類

① long bone

長骨：四肢にある長く伸びた骨（上腕骨，大腿骨）

② short bone

短骨：縦，横がほぼ同じ寸法の骨（手根骨，踵骨）

③ flat bone

扁平骨：薄く扁平な形の骨（肩甲骨，頭頂骨）

④ irregular bone

不規則骨：複雑な形をした脊柱の分節（椎骨）

⑤ pneumatized bone

含気骨：空洞あるいは多くの含気洞を含む骨（上顎骨，側頭骨乳様突起）

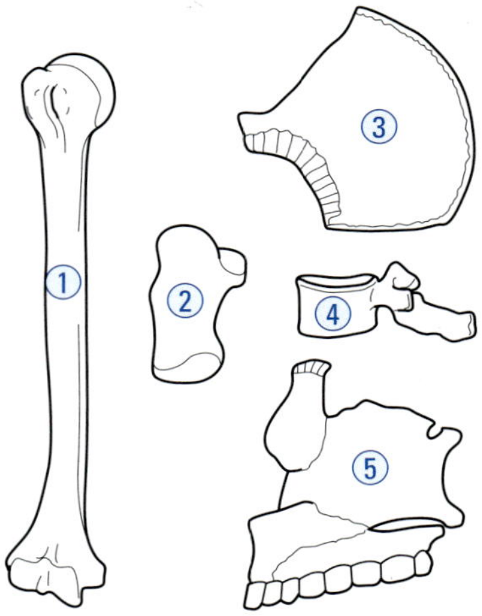

☆ これだけは覚えておきたい英語

- **spine, vertebral column**　脊柱
- **vertebra**　脊椎
- **vertebral disc; intervertebral disc**　椎間板
- **cartilage**　軟骨
- **(bone) marrow**　骨髄

EXERCISES

1. 日本語に相当する英語になるように，必要なアルファベットを補い，並べ替えなさい。

(1) eklnost 骨格 (　　　　　)
(2) abeemnr 膜 (　　　　　)
(3) eistu 組織 (　　　　　)
(4) aaceglrt 軟骨 (　　　　　)
(5) amorw 骨髄 (　　　　　)

2. (1)〜(5)の日本語に相当する英語を書き，その説明に該当するものをa〜eから選びなさい。

(1) 骨 (　　　　　) (　　)
(2) 軟骨 (　　　　　) (　　)
(3) 椎骨 (　　　　　) (　　)
(4) 脊柱 (　　　　　) (　　)
(5) 組織 (　　　　　) (　　)

a. Each of the series of small bones forming the backbone
b. The row of small bones that are connected together down the middle of the back
c. The strong white tissue in the joints that prevents the bones from rubbing against each other
d. Material consisting of specialized cells that makes up the different parts of the body
e. The hard, whitish tissue making up the skeleton

3. 以下の日常英語と同じ意味の英語を選びなさい。

(1) upper arm bone (　　)
(2) shoulder blade (　　)
(3) collarbone (　　)
(4) backbone (　　)
(5) skull (　　)

a. clavicle　b. spine
c. cranium　d. humerus
e. patella　f. scapula

Joints (articulations) 関節

骨端と骨端が可動性をもって連結している部分。連結の仕方は縫合，骨結合，軟骨結合，靱帯結合がある。関節の動きと働きは，その可動性の状態によって以下に分類される。

① **synarthrosis**（不動結合）：骨と骨がまったく動かない，あるいはほんのわずかしか動かない。
② **amphiarthrosis**（半関節）：骨と骨が膠原線維あるいは軟骨で結合し，ほとんど動かない。
③ **diarthrosis or synovial joint**（可動結合）：滑膜性で広範囲に動く。その構造は6つに分類される（次ページの図参照）。この連結のみを日本では「関節」とよぶ。

① femur	大腿骨
② synovial bursa	滑液包
③ tendon	腱
④ patella	膝蓋骨
⑤ fat pad	脂肪体
⑥ articular meniscus semilunar cartilage	関節半月
⑦ articular cavity	関節腔
⑧ intracapsular ligament	関節内靱帯
⑨ articular cartilage	関節軟骨
⑩ tibia	脛骨
⑪ extracapsular ligament	関節外靱帯
⑫ joint capsule	関節包
⑬ fibrous articular capsule	線維膜
⑭ synovial membrane	滑膜

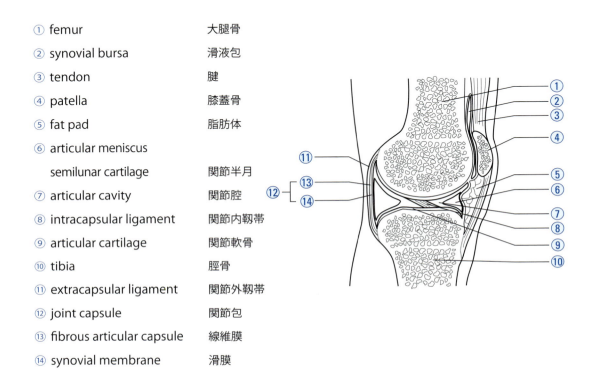

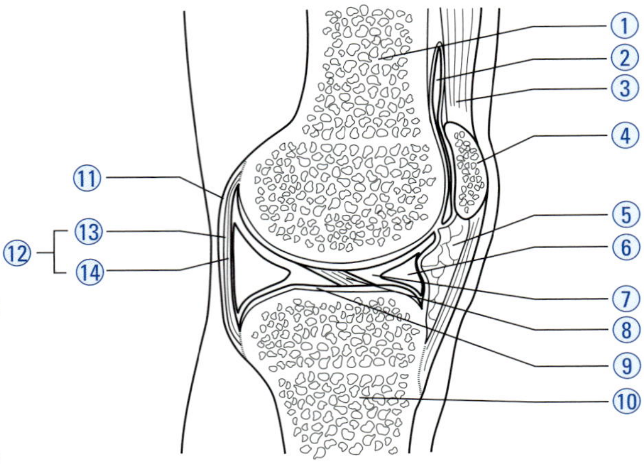

ことばのルーツ

bone 骨

boneは古期高地ドイツ語のbeinから古期英語（1150年頃以前の英語）bānを経て，boneに変化した。もとは手足の骨の意味である。

sacrum 仙骨

ラテン語のos sacrum（聖なる骨）から。いくつかの説があるが，いけにえとして捧げられたこと，あるいはこの骨は，死後長く原型をとどめるために，復活のとき（キリスト教では死後復活すると信じられている）この骨が中心になって再び肉体ができる，と考えられていたことによる。

Types of Joints 関節の種類

①

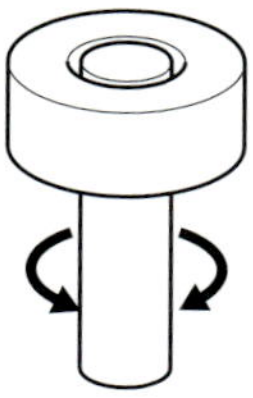

pivot joint　車軸関節
片方の骨の穴に，もう一方の突起した骨が入った形。突起を軸に動く。

②

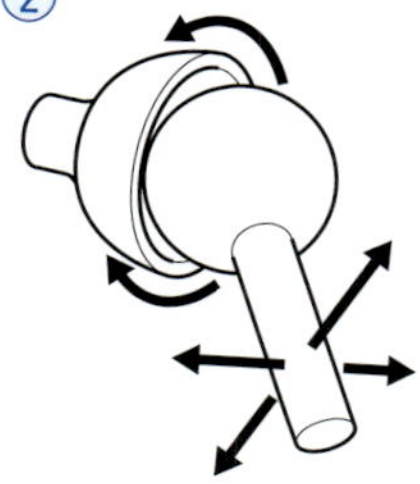

ball and socket joint　球関節
骨の片方がほぼ球形，もう一方が丸いおわん状で前後左右，回転運動を可能にする。

③

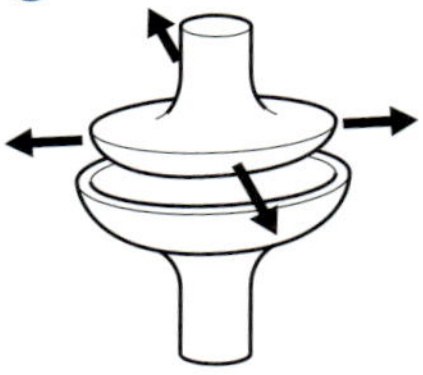

ellipsoid（condylar）joint
楕円関節
片方の骨も受ける骨も楕円形をしている。前後，左右の動きのみ可能。

④

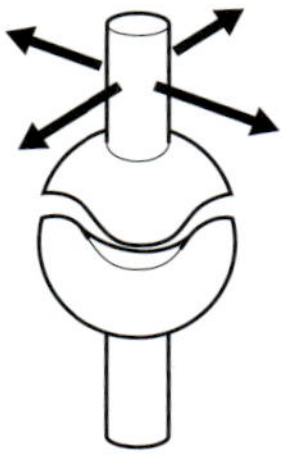

saddle joint　鞍関節
人が馬に乗った形に似ている。前後，左右の2方向のみの動きをする。

⑤

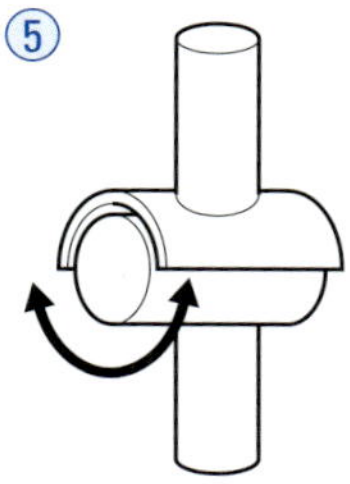

hinge joint　蝶番関節
ドアの蝶番に似た形をしている。曲げる，伸ばすという動きをする。

⑥

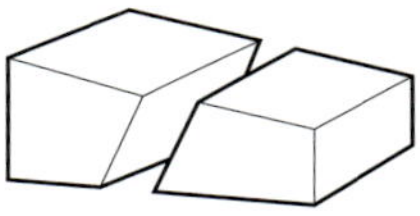

plane（gliding）joint
平面（滑動）関節
骨の両面がほぼ平坦で，互いにスライドする。動きは非常に小さい。

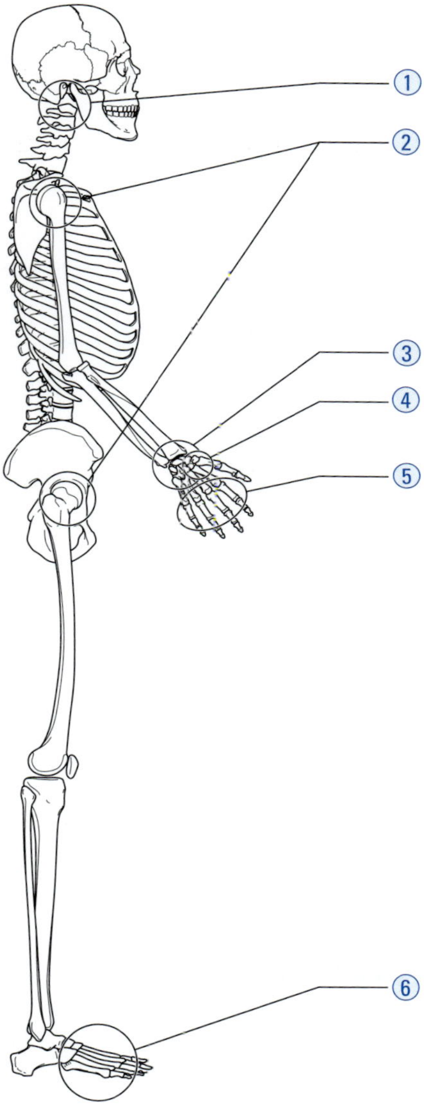

INTRODUCTION CHAPTER I CHAPTER II CHAPTER III CHAPTER IV APPENDIX

EXERCISES

1. 以下の関節に適切な図を選び，記号とそれぞれの日本語を書きなさい。

(1) ball and socket joint　(　)(　　　)

(2) hinge joint　(　)(　　　)

(3) pivot joint　(　)(　　　)

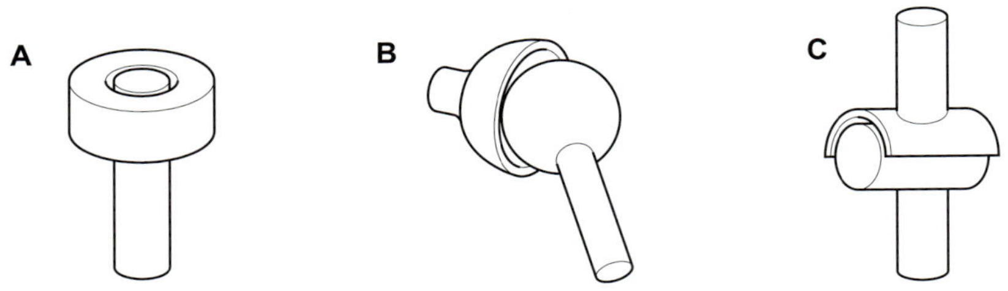

One-point Lesson

医学英語の常識

• 解剖学用語（Terminologia Anatomica, TA）

例えば，肋骨をribともcostaともいい，長骨をlong boneあるいはos longumという。いずれもTA（解剖学用語）であるが，公式語はラテン語である。TAは1903年以来，IFAA（国際解剖学会連合）によって検討され，1994年には多くの国で非公式ではあるが国際通用語として使用されている約1,000語を加えて，1997年，解剖学用語として約7,500語が承認された。用語集には，世界の意思疎通共通語として英語も収められている。

• ラテン語がなぜ解剖学用語なのか？

現代医学の歴史は，臨床観察と人体の構造を知ることから始まったといってよいであろう。解剖学用語にラテン語が多いのは，ギリシャのヒポクラテスに倣い発展した医学が，ほかの学術用語と同様にギリシャ語・ラテン語を用いたためである。

英語との違いは，例えば，os longum，ossa digitorumのようにラテン語では形容詞が名詞に後置することである。また，ossaはosの複数形であるが，ほかにもlarynges（単数形larynx：喉頭），vertebrae（単数形vertebra：脊椎），dialyses（単数形dialysis：透析），ganglion（単数形ganglia：神経節）のように，英語とは異なる決まった形式があることに注意。

• 医学英語の構成

特に，科学・医学分野では簡潔な表現が望ましいとされる。用語も同様である。inflammation of the membrane around the bone（骨周辺の膜の炎症＝骨膜炎）をラテン語由来あるいはラテン語式の医学英語では一語でperiostitisという。これは，peri -（接頭辞：周辺の）＋oste（骨）＋itis（接尾辞：炎症）と分析できる。

医学英語の構成は，**接頭辞　＋　連結形（語根）＋　接尾辞**である。

これらを意識すると，膨大な量の医学英語も多少なりとも覚えやすいであろう。

※連結形oste-は子音の前ではosteo-となる。語根はosteon。

The Muscular System 筋肉系

人体の筋（肉）は運動・伸縮に関わる骨格筋（skeletal muscle）と，主に内臓・血管壁を形成する平滑筋（smooth muscle），および特殊な心筋（cardiac muscle）の3種がある。それぞれ収縮のメカニズムは似ているが，内部構造が異なる。平滑筋には，他の2種にある横紋がない。一般に骨格筋を筋肉という。

BACKGROUND INFORMATION

Muscles make up almost 40%–50% of our body weight. When muscles work, they contract—become shorter and thicker. When muscles attached to bones contract, they exert a pull on the bones and cause them to move. Most muscles work in pairs—one set works while the other set rests. Voluntary muscles move and work when we want them to do so. Arm muscles, leg muscles, and neck muscles are examples of voluntary muscles. This kind of muscle has cells that are long, round, and cross-striped. Involuntary muscles continuously work whether we want them to or not. The nervous system controls involuntary muscles almost exclusively. The work of the stomach, intestines, lungs, and other internal organs is performed by involuntary muscles. This kind of muscle has cells that are slender, smooth, and without cross-stripes. Involuntary muscles are often called smooth muscles. A third kind of muscle is the cardiac muscle. This muscle is found only in the heart. Cells of the heart are striated both crossways and longways. Tendons attach muscles to bones. This connective tissue is very strong and flexible.

（Reproduced with permission from "The Human Body" by Edward P. Ortleb and Richard Cardice. Milliken Publishing Company, 1986）

収縮する，骨を引っ張る

随意筋

不随意筋

胃／腸／肺／内部器官，内臓

平滑筋

心筋

腱／結合組織

☆ これだけは覚えておきたい英語

• muscular system	筋肉系	• voluntary muscle	随意筋
• muscle	筋肉	• involuntary muscle	不随意筋
• skeletal muscle	骨格筋	• smooth muscle	平滑筋
• cardiac muscle	心筋	• tendon	腱

Outer Muscles 表層筋

anterior（前面）

①	trapezius m.	僧帽筋
②	deltoid m.	三角筋
③	pectoralis major m.	大胸筋
④	serratus anterior m.	前鋸筋
⑤	biceps brachii m.	上腕二頭筋
⑥	rectus abdominis m.	腹直筋
⑦	linea alba	白線
⑧	sartorius m.	縫工筋
⑨	tibialis anterior m.	前脛骨筋
⑩	extensor retinaculum	伸筋支帯

posterior（後面）

⑪	occipitofrontalis m.	後頭前頭筋
⑫	infraspinatus m.	棘下筋
⑬	teres major m.	大円筋
⑭	latissimus dorsi m.	広背筋
⑮	gluteus medius m.	中殿筋
⑯	gluteus maximus m.	大殿筋
⑰	semimembranosus m.	半膜様筋
⑱	biceps femoris m.	大腿二頭筋
⑲	gastrocnemius m.	腓腹筋
⑳	soleus m.	ヒラメ筋
㉑	calcaneal tendon (Achilles tendon)	踵骨腱（アキレス腱）
㉒	calcaneus	踵骨

［注］m. = muscle

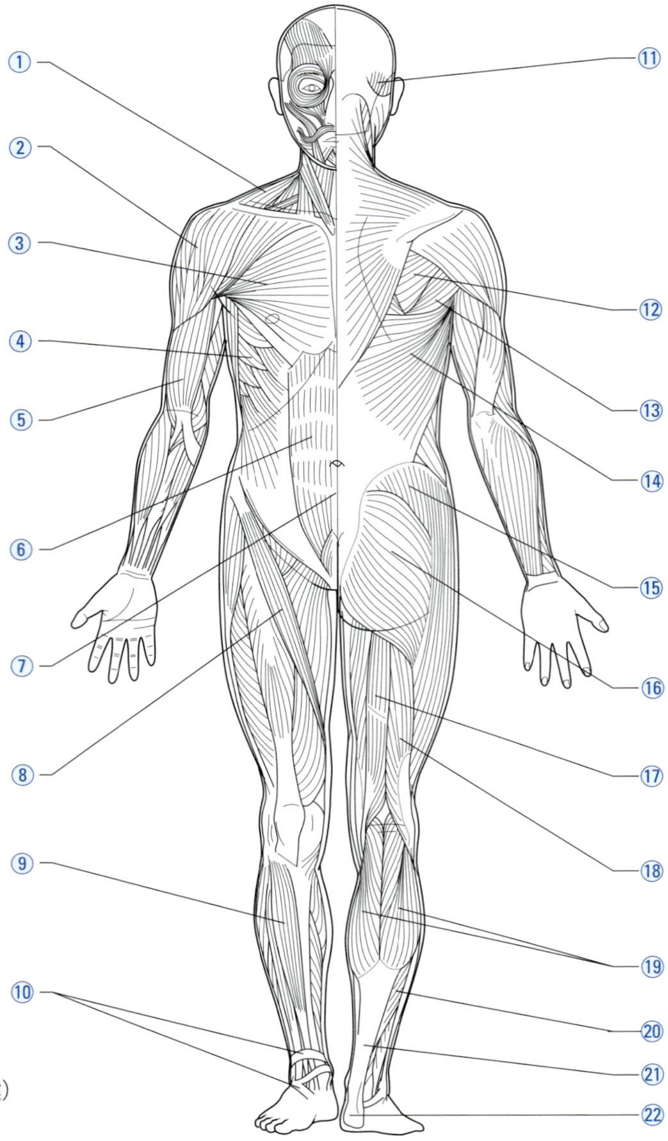

Types of Muscles 筋肉の種類

1）skeletal muscle 骨格筋（= striated m. 横紋筋，voluntary m. 随意筋）

骨に付着し，神経からの刺激を受け，収縮によって意志的に体を動かす随意筋。
筋細胞は長く円筒状で，横紋をもつ。多核。結合組織，血管，神経とともに存在する。

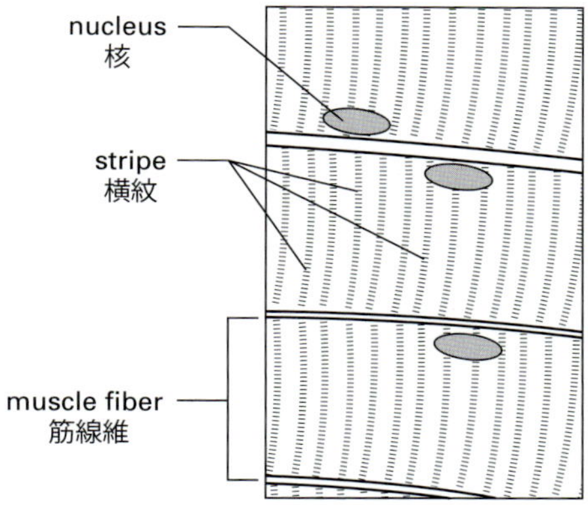

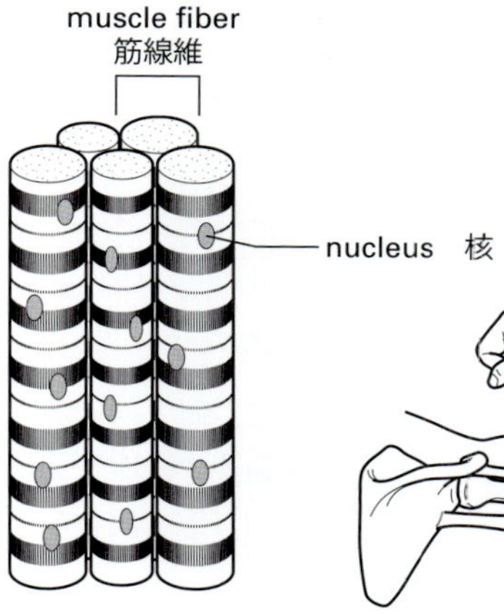

skeletal muscle
(voluntary muscle)
骨格筋（随意筋）

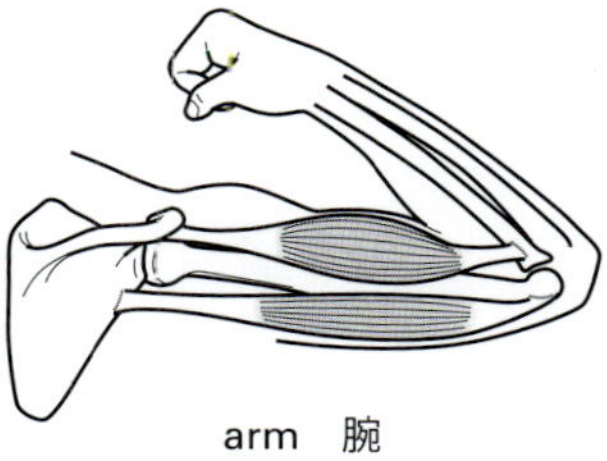

arm 腕

2）smooth muscle 平滑筋（= unstriated m.，involuntary m. 不随意筋）

自律神経系の支配を受け，随意に収縮できない。細胞は小さく，単核。
消化管，呼吸器，泌尿器，生殖器の壁にあり，運搬量を調節する。

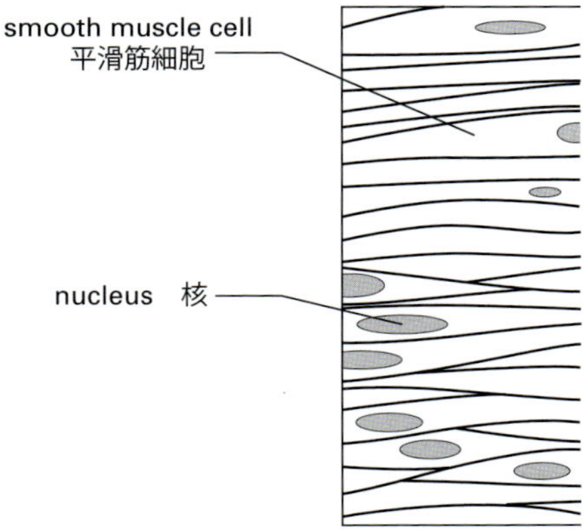

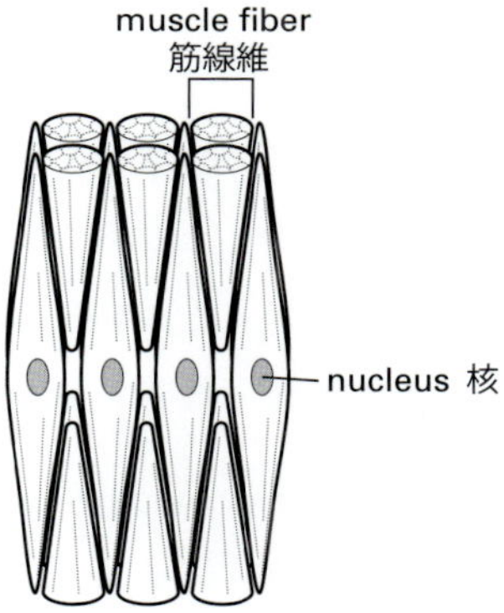

smooth muscle
(involuntary muscle)
平滑筋
（不随意筋）

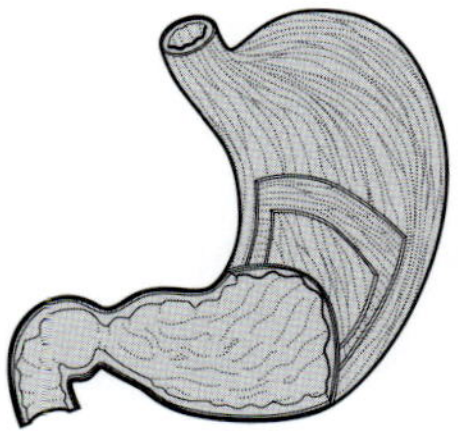

stomach 胃

3）cardiac muscle 心筋

心臓壁を形成する筋肉。骨格筋線維により横紋をもつ。
介在板によって広範に結合し，互いに連結して収縮を助ける。

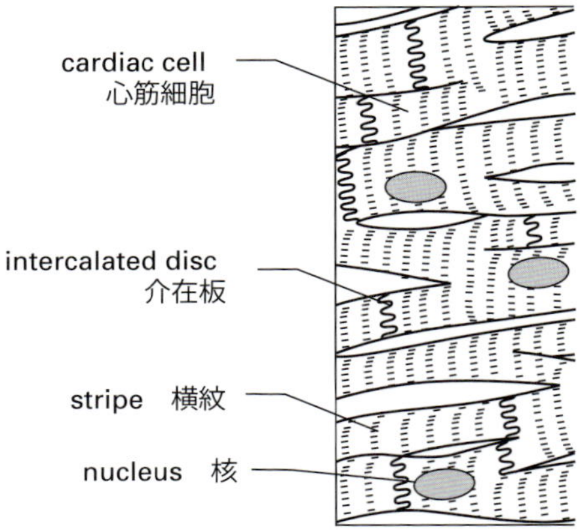

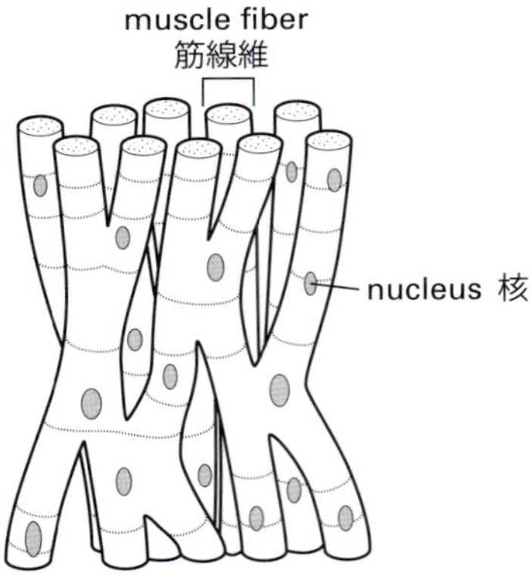

cardiac muscle
(involuntary muscle)
心筋（不随意筋）

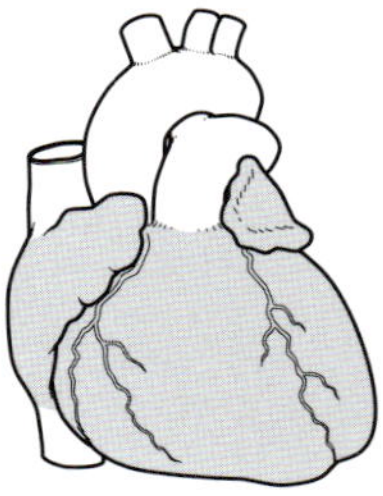

heart　心臓

One-point Lesson

筋肉の名称の覚え方

1. 位置を示す語を含む
   occipitofrontalis m.　後頭前頭筋：occipit-（後頭の）＋frontal（前頭の）
   tibialis anterior m.　前脛骨筋：ante-（前の）
   infraspinatus m.　棘下筋：infra-（下の）
2. 形を表す語を含む
   trapezius m.　僧帽筋：trapezium（不等辺四辺形，僧侶の帽子の形）
   serratus anterior m.　前鋸筋：serratus（ノコギリ歯状の，ギザギザの）
   deltoid m.　三角筋：delta（三角）＋-oid（～状の）
   soleus m.　ヒラメ筋：soleus（ヒラメ）
   rectus m.　腹直筋：rectus（まっすぐ）
3. 骨の名称を含む
   sternocleidomastoid m.　胸鎖乳突筋：sterno-（胸骨の）＋cleido-（鎖骨の）＋masto-（乳突の）＋ -oid
   anterior tibial m.　前脛骨筋：tibial（脛骨の）
4. 数字を含む
   biceps m.　二頭筋：bi-（2）＋-ceps（caput＝head）《筋頭が2つある》
   triceps m.　三頭筋：tri-（3）＋-ceps（caput＝head）《筋頭が3つある》
   semimembranous m.　半膜様筋：semi-（半）＋membranous（膜様の）

Bones, Muscles, Ligaments, and Tendons
骨，筋肉，靭帯および腱

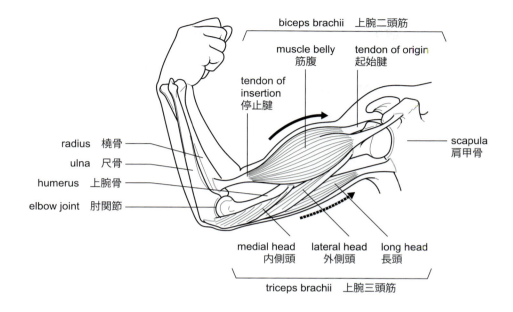

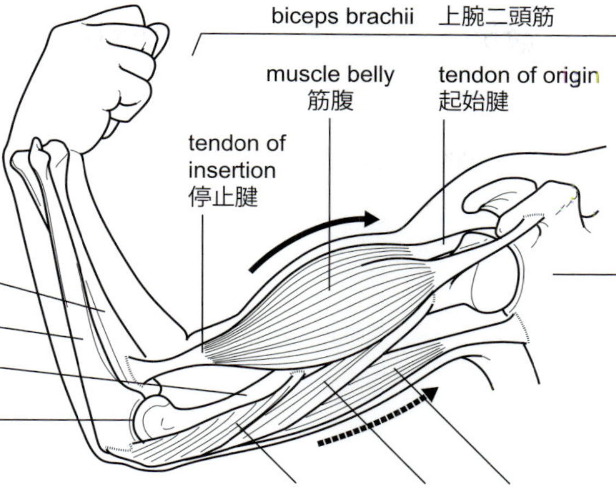
biceps brachii　上腕二頭筋
muscle belly
筋腹
tendon of origin
起始腱
tendon of insertion
停止腱
radius　橈骨
ulna　尺骨
humerus　上腕骨
elbow joint　肘関節
scapula
肩甲骨
medial head
内側頭
lateral head
外側頭
long head
長頭
triceps brachii　上腕三頭筋

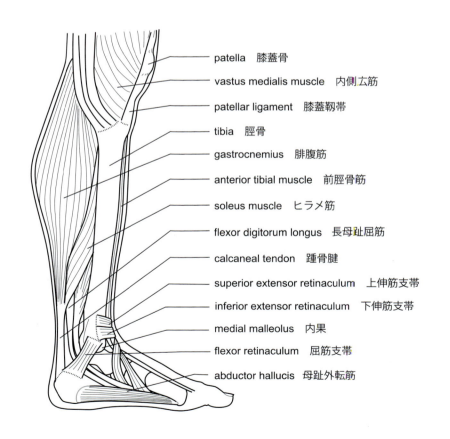

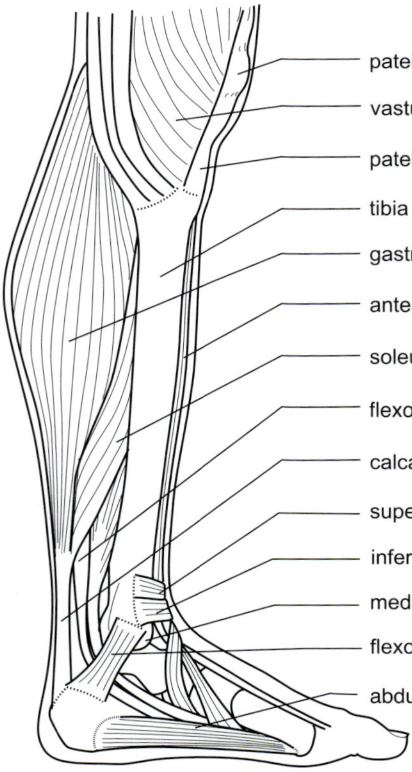
patella　膝蓋骨
vastus medialis muscle　内側広筋
patellar ligament　膝蓋靭帯
tibia　脛骨
gastrocnemius　腓腹筋
anterior tibial muscle　前脛骨筋
soleus muscle　ヒラメ筋
flexor digitorum longus　長母趾屈筋
calcaneal tendon　踵骨腱
superior extensor retinaculum　上伸筋支帯
inferior extensor retinaculum　下伸筋支帯
medial malleolus　内果
flexor retinaculum　屈筋支帯
abductor hallucis　母趾外転筋

Cervical muscles　頸部の筋肉

① splenius capitis m.	頭板状筋	⑪ digastric m. (the posterior belly	顎二腹筋 後腹）
② sternocleidomastoid m.	胸鎖乳突筋	⑫ digastric m. (the anterior belly	顎二腹筋 前腹）
③ levator scapulae m.	肩甲挙筋	⑬ hyoid bone	舌骨
④ trapezius m.	僧帽筋	⑭ thyrohyoid m.	甲状舌骨筋
⑤ scalenus medius m.	中斜角筋	⑮ omohyoid m.	肩甲舌骨筋
⑥ scalenus anterior m.	前斜角筋	⑯ sternohyoid m.	胸骨舌骨筋
⑦ scalenus posterior m.	後斜角筋	⑰ deltoid m.	三角筋
⑧ masseter m.	咬筋	⑱ pectoralis major m.	大胸筋
⑨ stylohyoideus m.	茎突舌骨筋		
⑩ mylohyoid m.	顎舌骨筋		

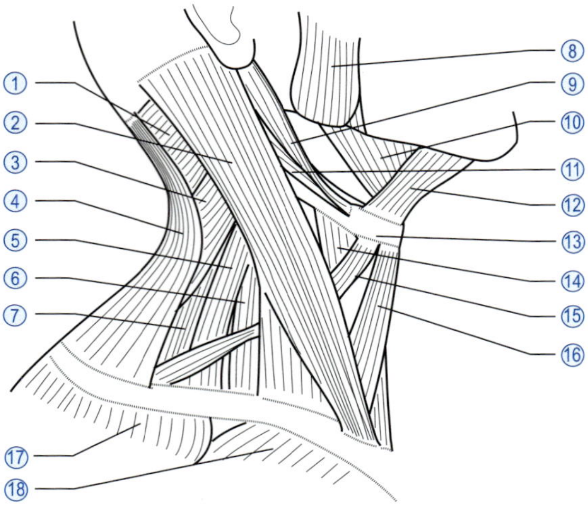

ことばのルーツ

muscle　筋肉

ラテン語のmusculus（ネズミ）が語源であるとされているが，明確ではない。筋肉が盛り上がるさまとネズミの動きが似ていることからの連想語とされる。musculusの-lusは指小辞（小さいものを表す接尾辞）である。

EXERCISES

1. 文字を正しい順序に並び替え，それぞれの日本語を書きなさい。

(1) celmsu　(　　　　　　) (　　　　　　)

(2) dennot　(　　　　　　) (　　　　　　)

(3) aegilmnt　(　　　　　　) (　　　　　　)

2. 空欄にa～cのいずれかを記入しなさい。また，それぞれの筋肉がある身体部位を書きなさい。

(1) (　　) have cells that are slender, smooth, and without cross-stripes.

(2) (　　) have cells that are long, round, and crossed-striped.

(3) The cells of the (　　) are striated both crossways and longways.

筋肉がある身体部位

a. cardiac muscles　(　　　　　　)

b. skeletal muscles　(　　　　　　)

c. smooth muscles　(　　　　　　)

INTRODUCTION
CHAPTER I
CHAPTER II
CHAPTER III
CHAPTER IV
APPENDIX

The Nervous System 神経系

身体の内部，表面のほとんどすべてにある神経終末にはレセプタ（受容器）がある。それらが刺激を受けると，情報は神経線維を介して中枢神経系に伝わり，中枢神経からの指令が運動神経を通って各器官へと伝達される。

神経系は，身体の各器官を連絡し，制御する神経組織の集合体である。脳と脊髄からなる中枢神経系（the central nervous system）とそれを身体末端につなぐネットワークとしての末梢神経系（the peripheral nervous system）からなる。身体の末梢の運動をコントロールしているのは脳の大脳皮質にある中心溝前部にある神経細胞で，後部は神経支配によるものである。

BACKGROUND INFORMATION

The nervous system functions to enable the body to respond to stimuli from the environment and to perform life functions. The functional unit of the nervous system is the nerve cell or the neuron.

The neuron consists of a cell body, which contains the nucleus and has numerous tree-like extensions called dendrites. These function to receive and conduct impulses toward the cell. A long fiber called an axon serves to conduct or relay the nerve impulses away from the cell body. What is frequently called a nerve is in fact a bundle of axons.

Stimuli are received by structures called receptors, which may be specialized for the reception of pressure, heat, cold, or other stimuli. Electrical and chemical changes in the neuron transmit the impulse from the dendrite to the axon. The gap between nerve endings of the axon and the dendrites of the next neuron is known as a synapse. The impulse is able to bridge this gap and pass from neuron to neuron until it terminates in a structure capable of reacting to the stimuli. This might be a gland or a muscle. These are known as effectors. When this impulse pathway includes passage through a nerve center, it is known as a reflex arc.

One division of the nervous system is the central nervous system, which consists of the brain and spinal cord. The cerebrum of the brain controls the higher processes and senses; the cerebellum controls the voluntary reflexes; the medulla

刺激（単数形 stimulus）
神経細胞
核／樹状突起
インパルス
軸索
レセプタ（受容器）
シナプス（接合部）
腺
反射弓
脊髄
大脳
小脳

controls the involuntary reflexes. The other division of the nervous system, the peripheral, consists of the cranial and spinal nerves and the autonomic nervous structure. This latter structure serves the internal organs and controls various activities such as digestion, circulation, respiration, excretion, reproduction, and endocrine gland activity.

(Reproduced with permission from "The Human Body" by Edward P. Ortleb and Richard Cardice. Milliken Publishing Company, 1986)

末梢〔神経〕

自律神経系

消化／循環／呼吸／排泄

生殖／内分泌腺

Classification of the Nervous System 神経系の構成

The central nervous system（CNS） 中枢神経系

すべての神経を連結する脳と脊髄からなる。

The peripheral nervous system（PNS） 末梢神経系

脳から脳神経が，脳脊髄から脊髄神経が末梢に行くことで，中枢神経系と皮膚・感覚器官・筋肉・腺などとを連絡する。神経節，感覚神経，自律神経，神経叢を含む。

The autonomic nervous system（ANS） 自律神経系

平滑筋，心筋，腺細胞（血管，心臓，胃腸，子宮，膀胱，内分泌腺，唾液腺，膵臓）などの運動性神経支配を行い，生体の植物的機能を自動的に調節する神経系。

The sympathetic nervous system（SNS） 交感神経系

脊椎動物の自律神経機能を調節し，神経興奮の伝達物質であるアドレナリン，ノルアドレナリンが生体を活動的にする。神経線維は脊髄の胸腰部側角から出て，脊柱の両側を走る交感神経幹に入る。そこから神経末梢が出て血管，皮膚，汗腺，内臓平滑筋，分泌線などに広く分布する。

The parasympathetic nervous system（PNS） 副交感神経系

脳神経と脊髄神経の一部から出る。頭部の神経節は動眼，顔面，舌咽，迷走にあり，体幹部内臓のほとんどに神経節があり，呼吸，消化，循環などを支配する。交感神経系と拮抗し，末端からアセチルコリンを分泌し，心臓には抑制的に，胃腸運動には促進的に作用する。ほか，血管拡張，瞳孔縮小，発熱発汗などの機能がある。

［注］末梢神経系は，解剖学的にはcranial nerves（脳神経）とspinal nerves（脊髄神経）に，機能的にはsomatic nerves（体性神経）とautonomic nerves（自律神経）に分類される。

☆ これだけは覚えておきたい英語

- **nervous system** 神経系
- **neuron** ニューロン
- **stimuli**（単数形**stimulus**） 刺激
- **spinal cord** 脊髄

Conduction of the Central Nervous System and Peripheral Nervous System

中枢神経系と末梢神経系の伝導路

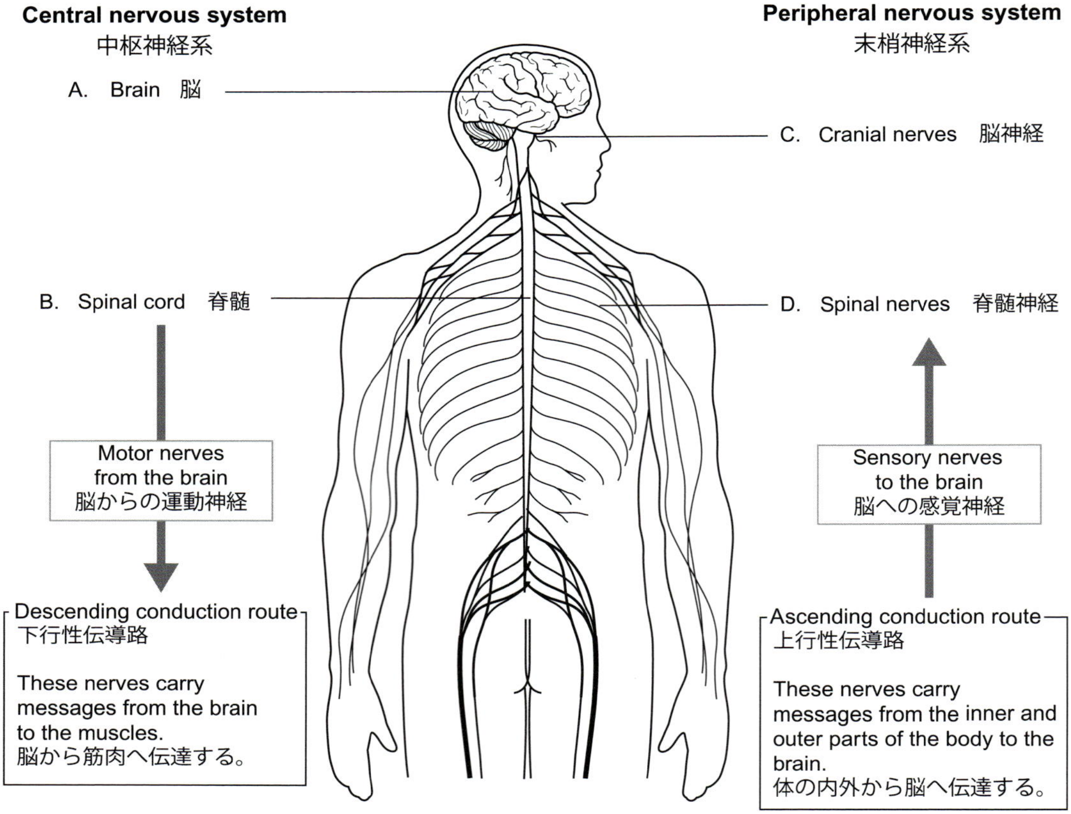

ことばのルーツ

arachnoid membrane　くも膜

くも膜は脊髄を被うspinal meninges（脊髄膜）の一つであり，硬膜（dura mater）と軟膜（pia mater）の間にある。水を含んだくもの巣のような形状から，ギリシャ神話に登場する少女Arachne（アラクネ）が自分の織物を自慢したために女神アテナの怒りをかって，くもに変えられた話に由来する。なお，dura materは「厳しい母親」，pia materは「優しい母親」という意味のアラビア語に由来する語である。

Peripheral Nervous System 末梢神経系

末梢神経は，体表や体内の各器官に分布し、中枢神経と情報のやり取りを行う。

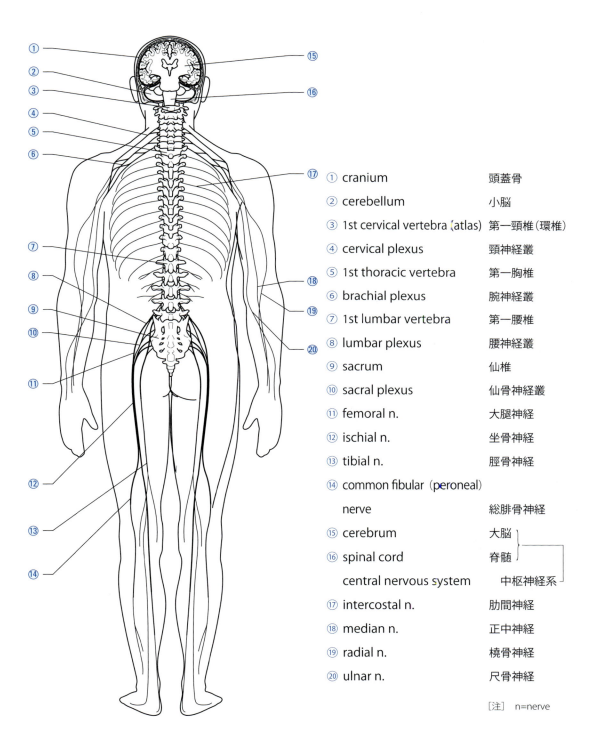

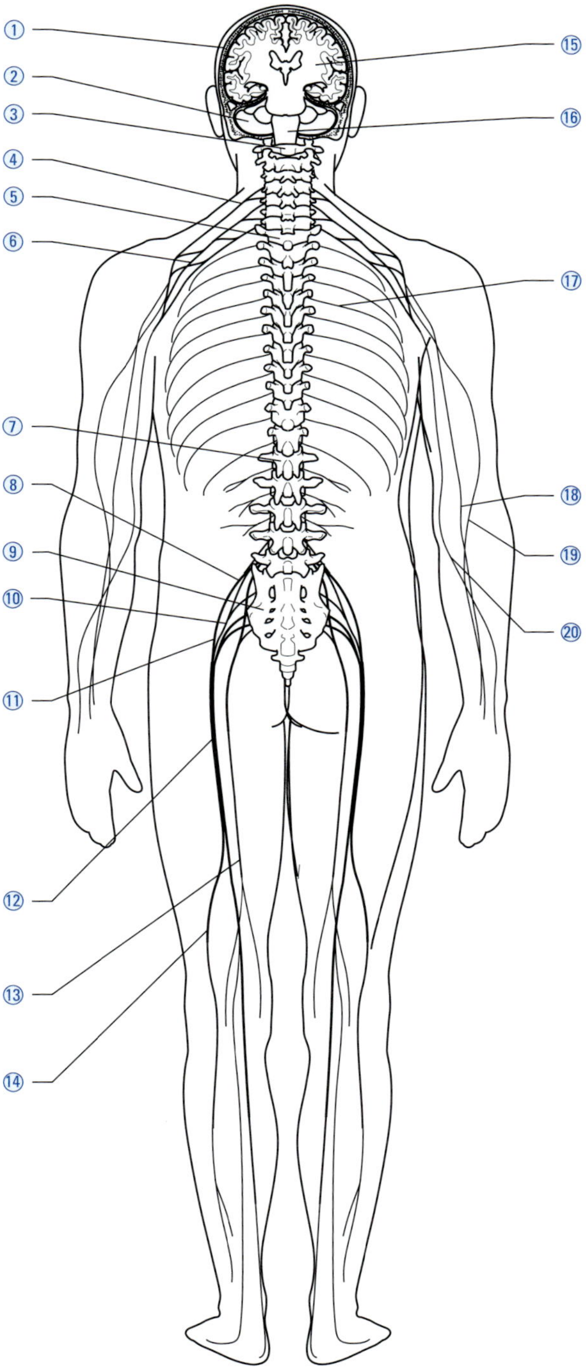

①	cranium	頭蓋骨
②	cerebellum	小脳
③	1st cervical vertebra (atlas)	第一頸椎（環椎）
④	cervical plexus	頸神経叢
⑤	1st thoracic vertebra	第一胸椎
⑥	brachial plexus	腕神経叢
⑦	1st lumbar vertebra	第一腰椎
⑧	lumbar plexus	腰神経叢
⑨	sacrum	仙椎
⑩	sacral plexus	仙骨神経叢
⑪	femoral n.	大腿神経
⑫	ischial n.	坐骨神経
⑬	tibial n.	脛骨神経
⑭	common fibular (peroneal) nerve	総腓骨神経
⑮	cerebrum	大脳
⑯	spinal cord	脊髄
	central nervous system	中枢神経系
⑰	intercostal n.	肋間神経
⑱	median n.	正中神経
⑲	radial n.	橈骨神経
⑳	ulnar n.	尺骨神経

［注］ n=nerve

Autonomic Nervous System 自律神経系と支配器官

脊柱と連結する神経系によって形成される神経である。身体の主要器官（心臓，肺など）の自律神経を調整し，人が睡眠中あるいは無意識のときにさえ機能する。ここでは交感神経系の神経支配を示す。

①	oculomotor nerve	動眼神経
②	facial nerve	顔面神経
③	hypoglossal nerve	舌咽神経
④	vagus nerve	迷走神経
⑤	eye	眼
⑥	cerebral artery	脳血管
⑦	parotid gland	耳下腺
⑧	sublingual gland	舌下腺
⑨	peripheral blood vessel	末梢血管
⑩	bronchus	気管支
⑪	heart	心臓
⑫	stomach	胃
⑬	liver	肝臓
⑭	pancreas	膵臓
⑮	small intestine	小腸
⑯	adrenal gland	副腎
⑰	kidney	腎臓
⑱	colon	結腸
⑲	urinary bladder	膀胱
⑳	genitalia	生殖器

㉑ preganglionic fiber 節前線維（実線）
postganglionic fiber 節後線維（破線）

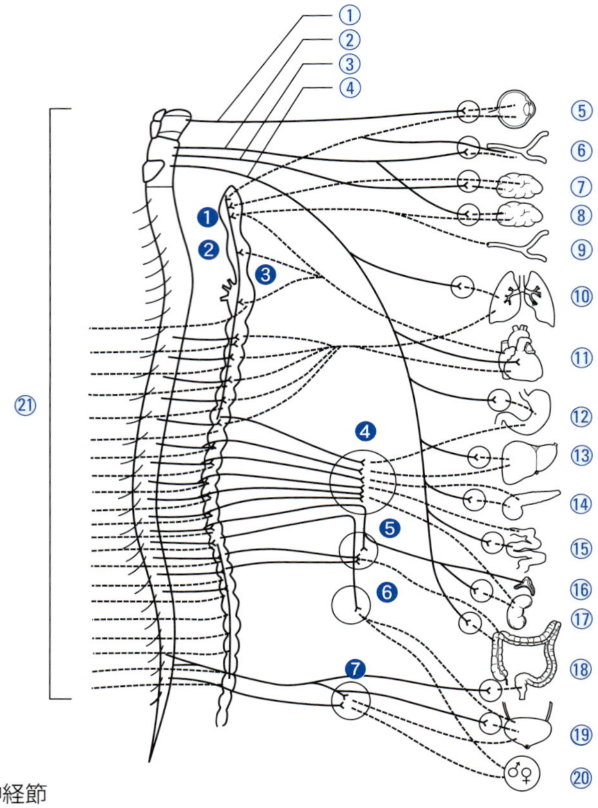

❶	superior cervical ganglion	上頸神経節
❷	middle cervical ganglion	中頸神経節
❸	inferior cervical ganglion	下頸神経節
❹	celiac ganglion	腹腔神経節
❺	superior mesenteric ganglion	上腸間膜神経節
❻	inferior mesenteric ganglion	下腸間膜神経節
❼	pelvic ganglion	骨盤神経節

Parasympathetic Nervous System 副交感神経系

2つある自律神経系のうちの1である。交感神経系に拮抗して作用し，心臓の活動を緩やかにし，血圧を下げ，消化管の蠕動を亢進させる。

① lacrimal gland　涙腺
② pupil　瞳孔
③ nasal mucosa　鼻粘膜
④ submandibular gland　顎下腺
⑤ sublingual gland　舌下腺
⑥ parotid gland　耳下腺
⑦ heart　心臓
⑧ esophagus　食道
⑨ lung and bronchus　肺・気管支
⑩ stomach　胃
⑪ liver　肝臓
⑫ kidney　腎臓
⑬ urinary bladder　膀胱
⑭ large intestine　大腸
⑮ rectum　直腸
⑯ accessory nucleus of the occulomotor nerve (the Edinger-Westphal nucleus)　動眼神経副核；エディンガー－ウエストファール核
⑰ superior salivatory nucleus　上唾液核
⑱ inferior salivatory nucleus　下唾液核
⑲ nucleus of the vagus nerve　迷走神経核
⑳ pelvic splanchnic nerve　骨盤内臓神経
㉑ sacral segment　仙髄

❶ ciliary ganglion　毛様体神経節
❷ sphenopalatine ganglion　翼口蓋神経節
❸ submandibular ganglion　顎下神経節
❹ otic ganglion　耳神経節
❺ celiac ganglion　腹腔神経節

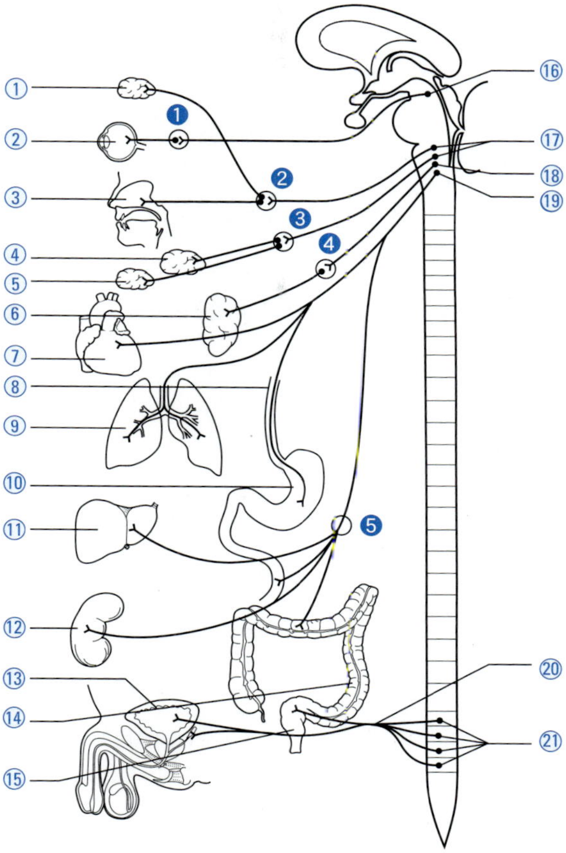

☆ これだけは覚えておきたい英語

- **central nervous system (CNS)**　中枢神経系
- **peripheral nervous system (PNS)**　末梢神経系
- **autonomic nervous system (ANS)**　自律神経系
- **nerve**　神経
- **cerebrum**　大脳
- **cerebellum**　小脳
- **spinal cord**　脊髄

INTRODUCTION CHAPTER I CHAPTER II CHAPTER III CHAPTER IV APPENDIX

EXERCISES

1. 以下の略語の完全形を書きなさい。

CNS ＝（　　　　　　　　　　　　　　　　　　　　　　）

PNS ＝（　　　　　　　　　　　　　　　　　　　　　　）

ANS ＝（　　　　　　　　　　　　　　　　　　　　　　）

2. 空白にアルファベットを記入し，英語を完成しなさい。

(1) d__g__s t__o__　　(2) c__r c__l a__i o__

(3) e__c__e__i__n　　(4) __e__e b__u m

(5) c e__e b e__ __u m　　(6) s p__n a l　c__ __d

3. 以下の用語を説明する英文をa～cから選びなさい。

(1) cerebrum　（　　）

(2) nerve　（　　）

(3) spinal cord　（　　）

a. Any of the structures that carry messages between the brain and other parts of the body, enabling you to move, feel pain, etc.

b. The part of the central nervous system that runs from the medulla oblongata to the terminal in the vertebral tunnel of the spine

c. The front part of the brain responsible for thoughts, emotions, and personality

4. 以下の文中の下線部に相当する英語を書きなさい。

(1) 神経系は，中枢神経系（　　　　　　　　　　）と末梢神経系（　　　　　　　　）に大別され，末梢神経系は構造的には体性神経系，機能的には自律神経系（　　　　　　　　）に分類される。

(2) 中枢神経系を構成するのは，脳（　　　　）と脊髄（　　　　　）である。

(3) 末梢神経系を構成するのは，12対の脳神経（　　　　　　　　）と31対の脊髄神経（　　　　　　　）である。

(4) 自律神経系は，交感神経（　　　　　　　　　　）と副交感神経（　　　　　　　）からなる。

5. 内容が正しい文にはTを，間違っている文にはFを記入しなさい。

(1) _____ The nervous system enables the body to respond to stimuli from the environment.

(2) _____ The neuron has a large number of vine-like extensions called axons.

(3) _____ Effectors receive stimuli.

(4) _____ The gap between the nerve endings of the axon and the dendrites is called a synapse.

(5) _____ Impulses pass from neuron to neuron until they reach a structure capable of reacting to the stimuli.

CHAPTER IV

Rehabilitation for People with Diseases and Other Conditions

CHAPTER IV

Rehabilitation for People with Diseases and Other Conditions
疾患とリハビリテーション

Bone Fractures 骨折

骨折とは，直接あるいは何らかの間接的な外力によって，通常は連続している骨のつながりを絶たれた状態である。外傷性の骨折は，①骨折の状態，②折れ方によって分類される。ほかに，外力の加わり方，特別な病因によっても分類される。

患者のリハビリテーションにおいては，良肢位を保つこと，また感染など合併症の防止に努力する。

BACKGROUND INFORMATION

A bone fracture is a break or crack in a bone. It is sometimes referred to as a loss of continuity in the bone tissue from any cause. Causes range from injuries sustained in traffic accidents to sports injuries and industrial accidents. The various types of fracture are listed in the figures and summarized on the next two pages.

切断／亀裂
継続性の消失

Patients with fractures have such symptoms as local discoloration or deformities, swelling, and pain in the affected area. They may also experience shock, fever, hematuria, or proteinuria. These symptoms often disappear after several days, but they can be followed by a special change called a callus, which is a thickened, hardened part of the skin or soft tissue.

局部的変色
変形／腫れ，膨張／障害を受けた場所
血尿 *cf.* hemato(血液)＋ur(尿)＋ia(病的状態)
たんぱく尿 *cf.* protein(たんぱく質)
仮骨

Although most fractures are the result of physical injuries, many are also caused by diseases that weaken the bones. These are called pathologic fractures, and they are often seen in patients with such conditions as bone cancer, osteoporosis, osteomyelitis, and vitamin deficiency disorders. Elderly people and children also tend to be susceptible to fractures, as their bones are easily damaged and liable to break.

病的骨折
骨粗鬆症
骨髄炎／ビタミン欠乏障害

Classification of Fractures　骨折の分類

1. 開放の有無による分類

（1）**closed (simple) fracture**　閉鎖（単純）骨折
骨折部分が体外に開放しておらず，皮膚が無傷の場合。筋骨格系の治療のみですみ，感染の危険性は低い。

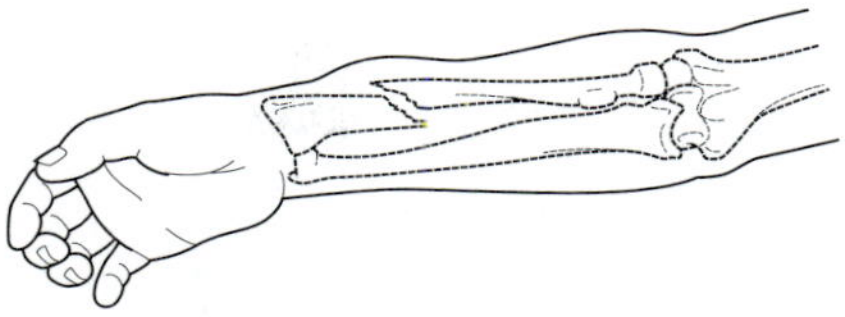

（2）**open (compound) fracture**　開放（複雑）骨折
骨折部分が体外に開放している。感染の危険性があるため，感染治療と筋骨格系の治療とを複合的に行うので，英語でcompound fracture（＝2種以上の，複合の）とよばれる。複雑に折れているという意味ではない。

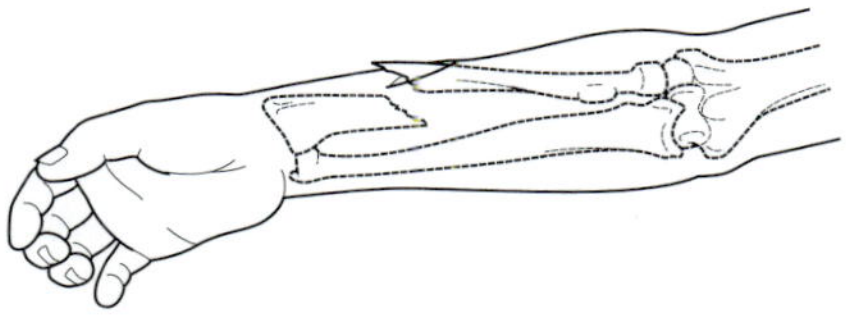

2. 骨の折れ方（骨折線走行）による分類

（1）**transverse fracture**　横骨折
棒を折るように折れる。

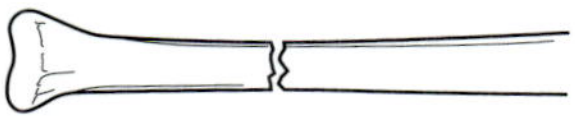

（2）**oblique fracture**　斜骨折
斜めに折れる。

（3）**spiral (twisted) fracture**　螺旋骨折
捻ったように折れる。

3. 外力のかかり方による分類

（1）**fissured (linear) fracture**　亀裂骨折
ひびが入る。

（2）**depressed fracture**　陥没骨折
頭蓋骨の一部が陥没する。

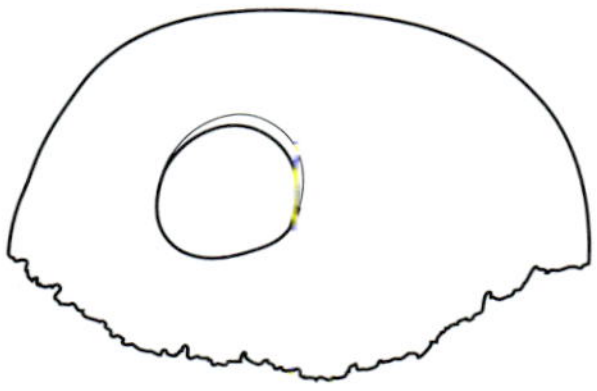

（3）**avulsion (sprain) fracture**　剥離骨折
軟部組織が引き離され骨片がともにはがれる。

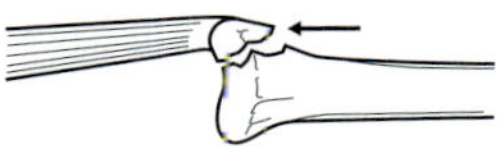

（4）**comminuted fracture**　粉砕骨折
骨が2つ以上の破片に砕かれる。

3. その他の要因による骨折

(1) 部位別の骨折

骨の部位と名称については，p. 38の骨格系の図を参照。好発部位は上肢，下肢，脊柱，手足，骨盤。

(2) 程度による骨折

complete fracture　完全骨折：骨のつながりが完全に途絶えている。

incomplete fracture　不完全骨折：骨が部分的につながっている。

(3) 特殊な要因による骨折

pathologic fracture　病的骨折：すでに存在する疾患，とくに骨そのものが腫瘍や壊死，骨粗鬆症のような疾患によって脆くなった骨の部位に起きる。

fatigue fracture　疲労骨折：外部から小さな力が骨に反復して加わり起きる。

compression fracture　圧迫骨折：軸方向の圧力によって折れたもの。通常，脊椎に起きる。

(4) 特定年齢に頻発する骨折

green-stick fracture　若木骨折：小児・思春期に起きる。柔軟性があるので，若木を折ったように骨が完全に破断しない不完全骨折。

epiphyseal injury　骨端線損傷：成長期に骨端，骨端線，骨幹端においてズレが生じる，あるいは損傷を受ける。

femoral neck fracture　大腿骨頸部骨折：高齢者に頻発する大腿骨頸部を折る骨折。

distal radius fracture　橈骨遠位端骨折：橈骨幹の遠位端に起きる骨折。

☆ これだけは覚えておきたい英語

- **(bone) fracture**　骨折
- **closed (simple) fracture**　閉鎖(単純)骨折
- **open (compound) fracture**　開放(複雑)骨折
- **osteoporosis**　骨粗鬆症
- **trauma**　外傷

Treatment of Fractures　骨折の治療

1. 応急処置　emergency treatment (first aid)

骨折部位を動かないように，パイプや定規，厚紙などの副子（副木，スプリント）で固定する。

2. 転移，変形（骨がずれる，曲がる）がある場合

徒手整復（manipulation）や器具による牽引（traction），非観血的整復術（closed reduction），あるいは観血的整復術（open reduction；手術で骨折端を整復する）を行う。

3. 固定　fixation

external fixation　外固定：ギプス，プラスチック包帯などによって骨折部が動かないように固定する。
internal fixation　内固定：手術によって骨折部を金属のプレート，ワイヤ，ねじ，釘などで接合し，安定化する。
external skeletal fixation　創外固定：骨折部周囲の骨に金属棒を串刺しにし，体外で固定する。開放骨折，粉砕骨折の際の感染防止に有効である。

〈リハビリテーション〉

骨折による関節の動きの悪化防止，治療期間中の安静，固定，運動不足などから生じる廃用変化を防ぎ止めるために，罹患部以外を早い時期に動かし始める。また，上肢は可動域の維持，下肢は負荷による歩行に努める。

〈骨折の合併症〉

aseptic necrosis	無菌壊死
fat embolism	脂肪塞栓症
Sudeck's atrophy	ズーデック骨萎縮
traumatic myositis ossificans	外傷性骨化性筋炎
Volkmann's contracture	フォルクマン拘縮

Therapeutic Exercises for Femoral Neck Fractures

大腿骨頸部骨折（術後）の運動療法

（イラストは柳澤　健（編）：イラスト理学療法ブラウン・ノート．メジカルビュー社，2007より引用）

足底背屈自動運動

Active plantar flexion and dorsiflexion of the ankle

深部静脈血栓予防のために，足関節底背屈自動運動を行わせる。

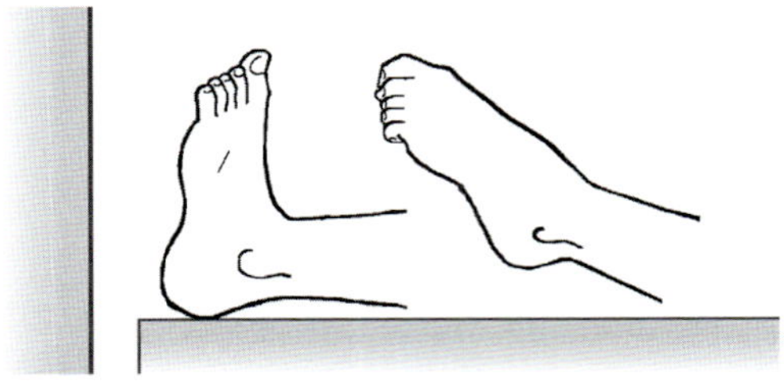

Instructions to the patient

I'd like you to lie down on your back. Now, keeping your heels on the bed, move your foot up and down at the ankle. Now, bend them back toward the wall.

仰向けに寝てください。まず，かかとをベッドの上につけてください。足首を上下に素早く動かしてください。次に，壁のほうへ伸ばしてください。

上肢の筋力増強運動

Training with a single pulley to strengthen the muscles of the upper extremities

上肢の筋力増強運動をする。

Instructions to the patient

Could you sit on the stool, please? Now, I'd like you to take hold of the hoop with your left hand and pull it down slowly. If you want to make it heavier, you can add more weights here. Now do the same thing with your right hand.

どうぞイスに座ってください。左手で輪をもってゆっくりと引っぱってください。もう一方の輪を重くすれば、より負荷のかかる運動をすることができます。次に，右手で同じことをします。

EXERCISES

1. 以下の日常英語と同じ意味の日本語を選びなさい。

(1) closed reduction	(　　)	a. 牽引
(2) fixation	(　　)	b. 開放骨折
(3) open fracture	(　　)	c. 非観血的整復術
(4) callus	(　　)	d. 固定
(5) traction	(　　)	e. 仮骨

2. 英語を説明する語句を選びなさい。

(1) avulsion fracture (　　)

(2) closed/simple fracture (　　)

(3) comminuted fracture (　　)

(4) open/compound fracture (　　)

(5) pathologic fracture (　　)

a. A fracture in which the skin is undamaged

b. A fracture exposing the bone to contamination

c. A fragmentary fracture caused by a bone-weakening disease

d. A fracture where part of the muscle is torn from the bone

e. A fracture resulting in several fragments

Chronic Low Back Pain 慢性腰痛

人はかつて立位になり，2足歩行を始めると，腰は体重を支えると同時に物を持ち，身体を伸び縮みさせることで最も負荷がかかるようになった。その結果，腰に痛みを覚えるようになった。その主症状は，脊柱の中央および下部の筋肉と関節の痛みであるが，痛み方は人によってさまざまである。原因も特定できないが，荷重による骨の変形，運動不足，筋肉疲労や胆石，腎臓の病気などの内臓疾患によるもの，さらにストレスのような精神的要因も考えられる。世代別では50〜80歳に多い。

BACKGROUND INFORMATION

Low back pain is considered to be chronic if it has been present for more than three months. Chronic low back pain can result from injury, disease, or stress on one or more anatomic structures, including bones, muscles, ligaments, joints, nerves, or the spinal cord. The affected structure sends signals through the nerve endings, up the spinal cord, and into the brain, where it registers as pain. The intensity of this pain ranges from mild to severe, and it may be felt in the bones, nerves, or muscles. The sensation of pain also varies, and patients may describe it as aching, burning, stabbing, tingling, sharp, dull, well-defined, or vague.

The cause of chronic low back pain is often unknown or impossible to specifically identify. In fact, in many instances, the condition or injury that triggered the pain may be completely healed and undetectable. But even if the original cause is healed or unknown, the pain felt by the patient is no less real, and physicians who specialize in treating such patients are well aware of this.

(Reproduced with modification from "http://www.knowyourback.org/Pages/SpinalConditions/LowBackPain/Chronic.aspx")

慢性の⇔acute（急性の）

解剖学的構造

神経終末（末梢知覚または運動神経線維の特殊終末）

軽度から重度まで

痛みの感覚

疼痛の／焼けるような／ずきずきする／ちくちくする／明確な

不確かな

医師，狭義で内科医

Notes

- **pain:** 痛み，疼痛。現実のあるいは潜在的な組織損傷を伴う不快な鋭い痛み，あるいは心因性の同様の苦痛。
- **ache:** 長く続く鈍い痛み。ほかに，distress: 精神的・肉体的苦痛，agony: 長く続く身体的・精神的な激しい苦痛。

☆ これだけは覚えておきたい英語

- aching　疼痛のある，うずく
- low back pain　腰痛
- nerve ending　神経終末
- anatomic structure　解剖学的構造
- intensity　(症状の) 強さ

Common Treatments for Chronic Low Back Pain

Many treatments focus on providing temporary relief from the pain, allowing the back to recover, or allowing the individual to participate in physical therapy to strengthen the back muscles. Typical examples of this approach are transcutaneous electrical nerve stimulation (TENS)❶ and epidural injections,❷ which are effective for many patients with back pain, but treatment often involves attempting several approaches to determine which ones are effective in managing pain in individual patients.

(1) Drug Therapy — drugs used to control low back pain include:

- ▶ non-steroidal anti-inflammatory drugs (NSAIDs) (Ibuprofen)❸
- ▶ adjuvant analgesics❹ (antidepressants and anticonvulsants)
- ▶ narcotics
- ▶ muscle relaxants — drugs with a sedative effect on the entire body
- ▶ oral steroids — suitable for short-term use

(2) Other Therapies

- ▶ traction
- ▶ epidural steroids — injected into the spine
- ▶ massage, biofeedback, acupuncture, ultrasound, meditation, herbal remedies, chiropractic manipulation, hot and cold packs.

Surgery is used only when the back pain is very debilitating and when there is a clear diagnosis of its cause. Typical categories are as follows:

一時的軽減
経皮的電気神経刺激
硬膜外注射
非ステロイド性抗炎症薬
補助的鎮痛薬
麻酔薬
筋弛緩薬
経口ステロイド類
牽引
生体自己制御／鍼／超音波／黙想
ハーブ療法／指圧手技／温・冷湿布

▶ disk removal — removing part of a herniated disk to relieve pressure on a nerve

▶ bone removal — removing bony growths that are pinching nerves

▶ fusion❺ — fusing vertebrae together to eliminate movement in the joints

癒合

Notes

❶ **transcutaneous electrical nerve stimulation** (TENS) **経皮的電気神経刺激〔法〕**

❷ **epidural injection　硬膜外注射**：脊髄・脳髄を覆い，骨を裏打ちする膜は，外から内へ硬膜(dura mater)，くも膜(arachnoid membrane)，軟膜(pia mater)があり，epiduralは「epi-（上の）+ dura mater（硬膜）+ -al（接尾辞，〜に関する）」という意味である。

❸ **non-steroidal anti-inflammatory drugs　非ステロイド性抗炎症薬**。鎮痛薬，解熱薬。
ibuprofen [àɪbjupróufən] **イブプロフェン**

❹ **adjuvant analgesics** [ǽdʒuvənt] **補助的鎮痛薬**：an-（接頭辞「不」）+ algia（「痛み」）+ -sics（接尾辞）

❺ **fusion　癒合**：2つの骨を合わせて1つにし，2つの骨の間の動きを少なくする。

☆ これだけは覚えておきたい英語

- **anti-inflammatory drug** 抗炎症薬
- **analgesic** 鎮痛薬
- **chiropractic manipulation** 指圧
- **sedative** 鎮静薬
- **traction** 牽引

ことばのルーツ

narcotics 麻酔薬・催眠薬・麻薬

narcoticsのnarco-は，ギリシャ語のnarkē（numbness: しびれ感，無感覚）に由来する。-icは名詞・学術名をつくる接尾辞で，-ticは-icの異形。-ticsは複数語形であるが，学術用語では通例単数扱いをする。

narco-で始まる語には，例えばnarcolepsy（睡眠発作），narcoanalysis（麻酔分析），narcosis（麻酔法）などがある。またギリシャ神話に登場するNarcissus（ナルキッソス）も同じルーツをもつ。彼は，泉の水面に映った自分の姿を美しい泉の精と思い込み恋をして，泉に落ちて死んでしまったnarcissist（自己陶酔者）であった。ここからnarcissistic personality disorder（自己愛性人格障害：DSM診断の一つ）という医学用語がつくられている。彼は優しい気質のnymph（ニンフ：半神半人の美少女の妖精たち）によって泉のほとりに葬られ，その場所からnarcissus（水仙）の花が咲いたとされる。水仙の球根には神経麻痺物質が含有されていることから，そう言われるようになったのだろう。しかし最も怖いのは，narcotic hunger（麻薬飢餓）を起こすnarcotic addiction（麻薬中毒）である。

Therapeutic Exercises for Low Back Pain

腰痛の運動療法

（イラストは柳澤　健（編）：イラスト理学療法ブラウン・ノート．メジカルビュー社，2007より引用）

骨盤後傾運動

Pelvic tilt exercise

腰椎の過前弯を減少させるために，骨盤後傾運動を行う。

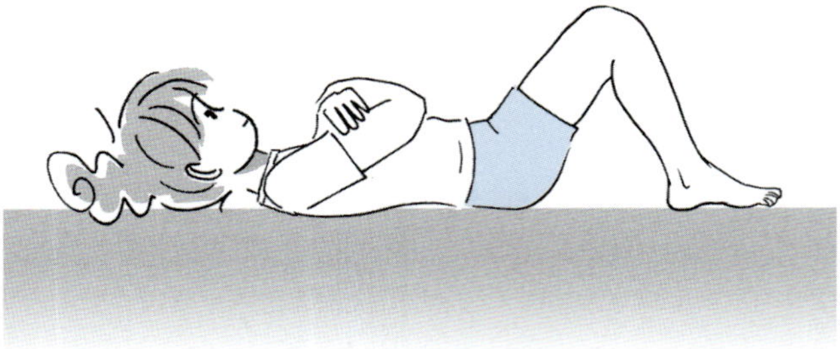

Instructions to the patient

First, please lie on your back on the floor with your knees bent. Now flatten your back against the floor as far as you can by tightening your abdominal muscles, and hold that position for 10 to 15 seconds.

膝を曲げて仰向けに寝てください。お腹に力を入れて腰部を床につけるように平らにしてください。そのまま10～15秒保ってください。

ハムストリングスのストレッチング

Hamstring stretch in the long sitting position

長座位で足趾を把持してハムストリングスのストレッチングを行う。

Instructions to the patient

First, you need to sit on the floor with your legs extended in front of you. OK, now bend forward slowly and reach for your toes. Good. Hold that position for 10 to 15 second. And sit up straight again. Now repeat the exercise several times.

足を伸ばして座ってください。次に足の指を持つように体を前に倒してください。そのまま10～15秒保ってください。それから元の位置に戻ります。この動作を数回繰り返しましょう。

腹筋運動

Abdominal muscle exercise with knees bent

腹筋を強化する。

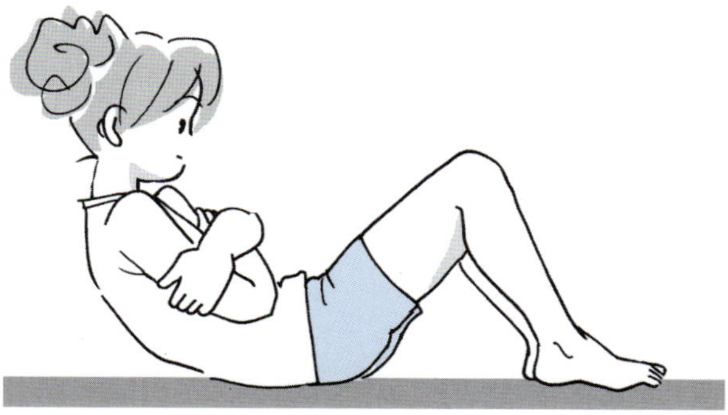

Instructions to the patient

I want you to lie face up on the mat with your arms crossed in front of your chest. Now, bend your knees and try to sit up. You may find this a little difficult.

マットの上に仰向けに寝て，胸の前で腕を組み，膝を曲げて上半身を起こしてください。この運動は少しきついかもしれません。

バランス練習

Exercise on all fours

骨盤の回旋や腰椎の過伸展が生じないように，対角線上に上下肢を挙上する。

Instructions to the patient

I'd like you to start off on all fours. Now, I want you to raise your right arm and point it straight ahead in front of you. Now, stretch your left leg out behind you. Try to hold this position for 30 seconds. Next, do the same thing with your left arm and right leg.

まず手と膝を床につけて四つ這いになってください。右腕と左脚を伸ばしてください。そのまま30秒間この姿勢を保ちます。この運動をもう一方の手と脚で繰り返します。

EXERCISES

1. (　)の中の文字を正しい順序に並び替えなさい。

(1) an （a m o t）ic ____________________

(2) c （h n o r）ic ____________________

(3) ch （a c i o p r r t）ic ____________________

(4) p （c h i i s y）an ____________________

(5) re （a a l n t x） ____________________

2. 内容が正しい文にはTを，間違っている文にはFを記入しなさい。

(1) _____ Low back pain is regarded as chronic when it has continued for more than six months.

(2) _____ Chronic low back pain is now possible to identify, because its cause has recently become known.

(3) _____ Chronic low back pain disappears when its cause is totally cured.

(4) _____ Chronic low back pain registers as pain in the spinal cord.

(5) _____ The only treatment for chronic low back pain is surgery.

Arthritis 関節炎

関節炎（arthritis）は，日本語も英語も文字通り「関節に炎症が起きる疾患」である。100種を超す関節炎があるが，一般的には，変形性関節症（osteoarthritis）と関節リウマチ（rheumatoid arthritis）が代表的である。前者は特に女性に頻発し，加齢に伴って軟骨に変性が生じる。後者は，全身の免疫異常によって関節部の炎症が生じ，腫れ，痛みの症状からやがて関節の変形へと機能障害をきたす。

BACKGROUND INFORMATION

Arthritis is a disease that causes painful inflammation of the joints, and rheumatism refers to any disease causing inflammation and pain in the joints, muscles, or connective tissue. On the basis of this definition of arthritis, more than 100 arthritic diseases are recognized. However, most people use the word arthritis to mean either osteoarthritis or rheumatoid arthritis.

リウマチ

結合組織《p.77参照》

変形性関節症
関節リウマチ

Osteoarthritis 変形性関節症

Osteoarthritis (OA) is more common than rheumatoid arthritis, and it involves the wearing down of the cartilage in the joints. Since cartilage provides cushioning, lubrication, and some stability to the joints, its loss is a significant problem. In extreme cases, the cartilage wears away completely, leaving bone rubbing on bone and causing extreme pain.

摩耗

潤滑

OA can be caused by extended wear and tear of the joints (usually in older individuals), or by injury to the joints. In the latter case, the injury often happens many years before arthritis develops. OA most commonly affects the hands, spine, knees, and hips. In the early stages, OA causes stiffness and mild pain after activity, which subsides with rest. As it becomes more advanced, the joint pain becomes severe, and in some cases it can be triggered by very small movements even when the patient is trying to rest. Individuals with OA have been reported to experience more pain right before a major weather change, but there is no evidence that a particularly cold or wet climate causes the disease.

硬直

Rheumatoid Arthritis 関節リウマチ

Rheumatoid❶ arthritis (RA) is an autoimmune disorder in which the immune system's❷ white blood cells attack the tissue lining the outer part of the joint. This lining is called the synovium,❸ which contains a fluid that bathes the joint (synovial fluid). The attacking white blood cells induce inflammation of the synovium, causing it to release inflammatory proteins as it thickens. Over time, the inflammatory proteins gradually damage the other tissues of the joint, including the bone, cartilage, ligaments, and tendons.

自己免疫疾患
免疫系
滑膜

Unlike with osteoarthritis,❹ the effect of RA on the joints is usually symmetrical: if, for example, the left knee is affected, the right knee is also likely to be affected. Although most individuals experience inflammation only in the joints, with the wrists, hands, ankles, and feet being the most commonly affected, RA can cause inflammation of tissues elsewhere in the body, including the lungs, heart, and even the blood vessels. Contracture❺ of the hands and fingers is common in advanced cases.

対称的な
拘縮

Lumps (rheumatoid nodules❻) may form under the skin of the hands, elbows, knees, back of the scalp, heels, or feet. The nodules may be as small as a pea or as large as a walnut, but they are usually not painful. Unlike the nodules caused by osteoarthritis, these nodules are not centered on the joints.

こぶ（リウマチ小結節）
頭皮

Notes

❶ **rheumatoid　リウマチ様の**：-oidは類似を表す接尾辞。
juvenile (rheumatoid) arthritis 若年性関節炎，若年性関節リウマチは小児期に発生し，ほとんどが消滅する。関節炎が持続すると関節の変形が起こることがある。

❷ **the immune system　免疫系**：免疫機構。体外から侵入した異物，感染細菌，あるいは体内の異常な細胞などに対する防御のしくみ。

❸ **synovium　滑膜**＝synovial membrane

❹ **osteoarthritis　変形性関節症**：oste- は骨に関する，arthr- は関節に関する連結形。それぞれのギリシャ語根は，osteon, arthron。-itisは炎症を意味する接尾辞。類語にdegenerative arthritis, degenerative joint disease。

❺ **contracture　拘縮**：筋肉や腱の異常な緊張あるいは線維化などによって関節が動かなくなること。

❻ **nodule　小結節**：nodus（語源は結び目）の指小辞。-leは「小さい」の意の接尾辞。

Common Treatment

Treatment of osteoarthritis and rheumatoid arthritis generally focuses on the control of pain. Most of the treatments are conservative,❶ meaning that they do not involve surgery or the administration of powerful drugs. The most common treatments are listed below.

保存的な

▶ A combination of rest and exercise—although too much rest can damage the joints, it helps maintain weight and range of motion, and reduces pain. Finding the right balance of rest and exercise can be a challenge. A daily walk or swim is strongly encouraged.

可動域

▶ Assistive devices❷— splints, braces, and walking sticks can reduce the load placed on the joints and provide some relief.

補助装具／副子，副木，スプリント／装具／杖
負荷

(Reproduced with permission from Handbook of Disabilities by RCEP at the University of Missouri. <http://www.rcep7.org/framefretxt.html>)

connective tissue　結合組織

結合組織は多数の細胞を伴う線維と基質から形成される，多様な組織である。人体の体腔にある器官を結びつけて安定させ，層は血管，リンパ管，神経などの通路となっている。関節部分の結合組織は下図を参照。

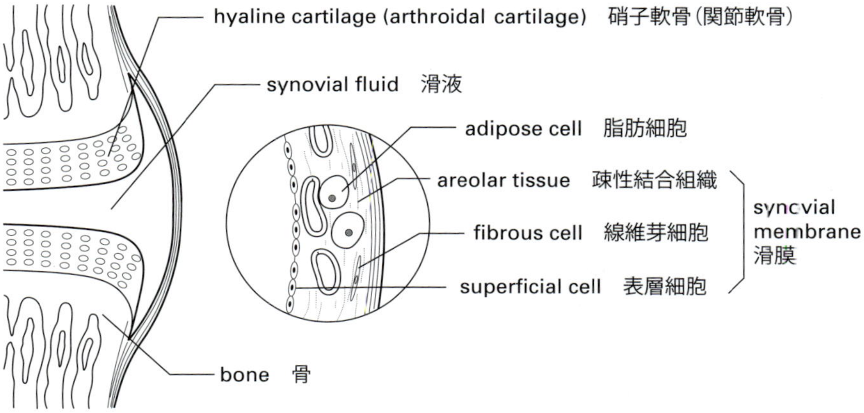

Notes

❶ **conservative treatment　保存療法**：外科手術，強い薬物投与をしない等，生体に及ぼす侵襲の程度を最小限に留めるように工夫して行う治療法。

❷ **assistive devices　補助器具・装置**

Other treatments

proper diet	適切な食事
heat/cold therapy	温熱／冷却療法
massage	マッサージ
relaxation	休養
acupuncture	鍼（はり）
surgery	外科手術
medication for pain	痛みの抑制薬

▶aspirin（アスピリン），non-steroidal anti-inflammatory drugs（NSAIDs＝非ステロイド性抗炎症薬），corticosteroids（コルチコステロイド類）など（副作用を注意しながら投与）。

☆これだけは覚えておきたい英語

- **connective tissue** 結合組織
- **contracture** 拘縮
- **immune system** 免疫系
- **osteoarthritis** 変形性関節症
- **rheumatoid arthritis** 関節リウマチ

ことばのルーツ

osteoarthritis　変形性関節症

osteoarthritisのoste（o）-は，ギリシャ語のosteon（骨）に由来する（p. 76のNotes参照）。このように，語尾が-onで終わる名詞からつくられる連結形は，ほかにもarthron→arthr(o) -；関節，neuron→neur（o）-；神経単位（ニューロン），skeleton→skelet(o)；骨格，などなど。日常語にも，phenomenon（現象），colon（句読点〔コロン〕），ion（イオン），icon（コンピュータのアイコン）など，ギリシャ語由来のものがある。

ラテン語のos（骨）は既述のように，例えばos coxae（寛骨）という形で，解剖学用語として現在も用いられている。

Therapeutic Exercises for Osteoarthritis of the Knee Joints
変形性膝関節症の運動療法

（イラストは柳澤　健（編）：イラスト理学療法ブラウン・ノート．メジカルビュー社，2007より引用）

下腿遠位部への軽い抵抗

Resistance exercise for the distal lower leg

座位で重錘バンドを足首につけ，下腿遠位部に軽い抵抗が加わるようにする。

Instructions to the patient

Just put this weight band around your ankle. Now, sit on the bench and raise your leg slowly, straightening it as you go. This exercise helps build your lower leg strength.

まず重錘バンドを足首につけてください。イスに座ってゆっくりと脚を挙げてください。この運動は下肢の筋肉を強化します。

杖の使用

Using a cane

杖を使用する。

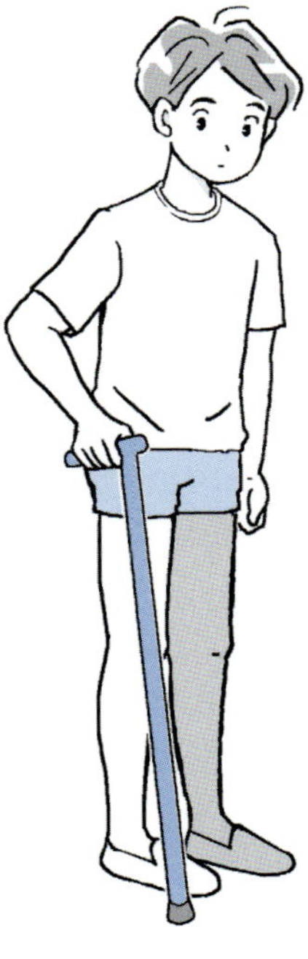

Instructions to the patient

If you use a cane, it will help reduce weight on your joints.

杖を持って歩きましょう。杖によって関節への体重の負担を減らすことができます。

膝の伸展

Knee extension exercise

長座位になり膝を軽く押しながら伸展させる。

Instructions to the patient

I'd like you to sit on the floor with your legs in front of you. Now, reach forward slowly and push your knees to straighten your leg.

床に座って，脚を前に伸ばしてください。手で膝をゆっくり押して伸ばしましょう。

Therapeutic Exercises for Rheumatoid Arthritis
関節リウマチの運動療法

等尺性収縮による筋力増強

Isometric contraction exercise to build muscle strength

等尺性収縮によって筋力を増強する。

［注］isometric contraction: 筋の長さを一定に保った状態で発生する力。

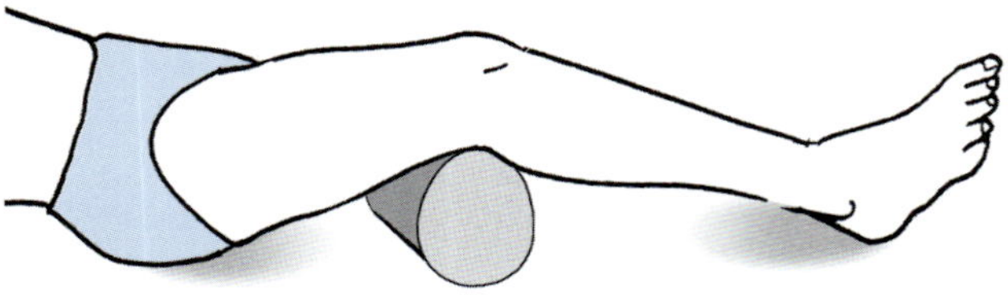

Instructions to the patient

Could you lie on your back, and I'll just place this cushion under your knees? Now, I want you to try to push down against the cushion without lifting your heels off the floor.

仰向けになりクッションを膝の下に置きます。かかとを床から浮かさずにクッションを下に押しつけてください。

立ち上がり練習

Push-up exercise to prepare for standing up

ひとりで立ち上がる訓練をする。

Instructions to the patient

Just sit on this chair with your forearms on the table in front of you. Now, support yourself with your arms, and try to raise your bottom from the chair.

テーブルに前腕を乗せて座ってください。テーブルにつけた腕で体を支えながらお尻をもち上げてください。

［注］車椅子の椅子部分をクッションで高くし，立ち上がり動作を補助することもある。

手指の筋力増強

Hand muscle strengthening exercise

手指の筋力を増強する。

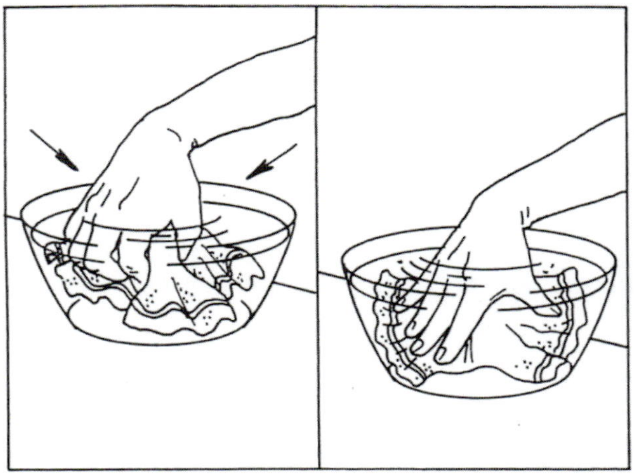

Instructions to the patient

Grab the washcloth with your right hand and spin it around in the bowl with your fingers as fast as you can. Next, spread your fingers out and keep turning it slowly. This exercise will help you coordinate your finger movements.

タオルを持ってできるかぎり速く円を描くように回してください。次に，指を広げ，タオルをゆっくりと回し続けます。指をスムースに動かす練習になります。

INTRODUCTION
CHAPTER I
CHAPTER II
CHAPTER III
CHAPTER IV
APPENDIX

INTRODUCTION CHAPTER I CHAPTER II CHAPTER III CHAPTER IV APPENDIX

EXERCISES

1. (　　) の文字を正しい順序に並び替え，語に相当する日本語を書きなさい。

(1) (a e h o o r r s t t) itis (　　　　　　　　) (　　　　　　　　)

(2) (a e h m r t u) oid (　　　　　　　　) (　　　　　　　　)

(3) i (e m m n u) (　　　　　　　　) (　　　　　　　　)

(4) s (i n o v y) um (　　　　　　　　) (　　　　　　　　)

(5) (o p r t) ein (　　　　　　　　) (　　　　　　　　)

2. (1)～(5)の用語の説明に該当するものをa～eから選びなさい。

(1) arthritis (　　)

(2) contracture (　　)

(3) immune (　　)

(4) rheumatism (　　)

(5) tissue (　　)

a. General term for pain and stiffness in the joints and muscles

b. Material that makes up the various parts of the body

c. A disease that makes the muscles and joints painful, stiff and swollen

d. Permanent tightening of a muscle caused by fibrosis

e. Having a natural resistance to specific infections

3. 英文が変形性関節症の症状を説明するものにはa，関節リウマチの症状を説明するものにはbを記入しなさい。

(1) (　　　) Contracture of the hands and fingers is very common.

(2) (　　　) The joints of the hands, spine, knees, and hips are commonly affected.

(3) (　　　) If a joint on one side of the body is affected, the corresponding joint on the other side is also likely to be affected.

(4) (　　　) In the early stages of the disease, patients experience mild pain after physical activity.

(5) (　　　) The severity of the pain depends on the extent to which the cartilage has worn away.

Sports Injury スポーツ傷害

主として競技をする運動選手に起きるスポーツ傷害(sports injury)は，外傷(physical trauma)と障害(disorder)に分類される。外傷は，いわゆる怪我とよばれ，競技中に発生する事故によって身体に損傷を受けるものである。障害は，長期にわたる身体の酷使(overuse)が原因で起きる疾気・故障である。

Achilles Tendon Rupture アキレス腱断裂

Achilles tendon rupture occurs in an area about 6 cm above the insertion on the calcaneus bone. It is most commonly observed in men in their 30s, and the male-to-female ratio of those who suffer it is nearly 20:1. Ruptures, which can be partial or full, often occur during sporting activities, when, for example, an athlete suddenly sprints, jumps up and down, or stretches the tendon while running, skiing, playing basketball, and so on. When the tendon ruptures, the patient feels acute pain, as if someone had kicked him/her behind the ankle, and the rupture is often accompanied by a sudden explosive popping sound. The patient cannot walk properly, and in the case of a complete rupture, a depression develops in the skin that has been torn. Most Achilles tendon ruptures occur when athletes make sudden, drastic changes to their training regimes, so clearly, such changes should be avoided.

筋肉などの付着点／踵骨腱=アキレス腱

陥凹

Treatment and Therapy

Although controversy has long surrounded the question of whether Achilles tendon rupture should be treated surgically or nonsurgically, no definitive conclusions have yet been reached. Commonly, a conservative, nonsurgical approach is taken.

As almost 50% of Achilles tendon ruptures are degenerative, orthosis, such as an equinus cast (which keeps the foot pointing downwards to oppose the ends of the ruptured tendon), are often used. If patients start rehabilitation two weeks after such conservative treatment begins, they usually make a quick recovery.

退行性

保存治療

Surgical options include open procedures (tendon sutures) or minimally invasive open and percutaneous techniques. Surgery generally offers a lower risk of re-rupture, but it entails the risk of infection and problems with wound-healing. Furthermore, physical therapy and rehabilitation after surgery are generally less effective than they are with nonsurgical approaches.

腱縫合

経皮的

One-point Lesson

Rules for Treatment of Sports Injury
スポーツ外傷の治療ルール

R	Rest	休息
I	Ice	冷却
C	Compression	圧迫
E	Elevation	挙上

T	Talk	話しかける
O	Observe	観察する
T	Touch	触れる
A	Active movement	自動運動
P	Passive movement	他動運動
S	Skill Test	スキルテスト

ことばのルーツ

Achilles tendon　アキレス腱

ギリシャ神話に登場する英雄アキレウスにちなむ。母ティティスは「戦争に出陣すれば必ず死ぬであろう」という神託を受け，その運命を避けようとして赤ん坊のアキレ(ウ)スをスティクス(Styx)川に浸け，不死身とした。彼は，トロイ戦争に出陣。獅子奮迅の活躍をしたが，敵方パリスの矢に足首を射られて戦死した。ティティスが足首を持って川に浸けたため，足首だけ生身だったのである。このことから，「誰にでも弱点はある」という意味で比喩的に「アキレス腱」と言う。

Dislocated Shoulder 肩関節脱臼

A dislocated shoulder, or glenohumeral dislocation, is an injury in which the upper arm bone (the humerus) becomes separated from the shoulder blade at the glenohumeral joint. The shoulder is the body's most mobile joint, which makes it vulnerable to dislocation.

The fibrous tissue that joins the bones of the shoulder is also easily stretched or torn, often complicating the dislocation. Dislocated shoulders most commonly occur in people playing contact sports, such as rugby, American football, hockey, and judo, but it can also occur when people are taking part in such sporting activities as volleyball, skiing, and gymnastics. In addition, falling down stairs, tossing and turning in bed, and stumbling on such obstructions as doorsteps are common causes of shoulder dislocation.

When the shoulder is dislocated in young people, the joint capsule sometimes flakes off or is torn, whereas the muscles surrounding the shoulder joint on the head of the humerus (the rotator cuff) tend to break and damage the nerves in the elderly people.

Shoulder dislocations are classified into three categories: anterior, posterior, and inferior dislocations. Over 95% of shoulder dislocations are of the anterior type, and most of these are subcoracoid.

The characteristic symptoms are sharp, tingling pain, swelling, bruising, and immovable joints, and the fact that the shoulder is out of place is often visible. Patients also often experience numbness and weakness in the neck or arm.

上腕骨
線維組織
体操
つまずくこと
剥がれ落ちる
上腕骨頭
前方，後方，下方脱臼
ちくちくする痛み
打撲傷
肩はずれ
麻痺

Treatment and Therapy

The first thing the patient must to do is consult a doctor as soon as possible. Failing this, reduction, which is the best treatment for dislocation, is difficult to perform because of swelling.

The main treatments for dislocated shoulders are closed and open reductions. Closed reduction includes immobilizing the shoulder with a sling or shoulder immobilizer so that the patient cannot use his/her arm. It is very important not to move the shoulder or force it back into place for two or three weeks after a shoulder dislocation is diagnosed. Doing so can damage the shoulder joint as well as its surrounding muscles, ligaments, nerves, and blood vessels. Reduction must be performed slowly because of the many risks involved.

閉鎖・開放整復

To control pain, anti-inflammatory drugs are generally used, though icing the shoulder can also help to reduce the pain and swelling associated with the injury by controlling internal bleeding and the buildup of fluids in and around the shoulder joint.

抗炎症薬

軽減する

Once someone has experienced a dislocated shoulder, the joint may become unstable and liable to repeat dislocations (recurrent dislocations). If the joint does not heal well, surgery is indicated.

反復性脱臼

After the pain and swelling resolves, a rehabilitation program is started to restore the range of motion of the shoulder and strengthen the muscles to prevent recurrent dislocation. Rehabilitation exercises start with simple arm motions. Closed reduction, including scapular manipulation, external rotation, and traction-countertraction, is continued to help the bones return to their normal position without surgery.

徒手整復

Sprained Ankle 足関節捻挫

A sprain is the stretching or tearing of a ligament and joint capsule surrounding a joint that usually results from a sharp twist. Sprains do not appear on X-ray images, which allows physicians to differentiate them easily from fractures and dislocations. A similar word, strain, is a tearing or stretching of a tendon or a muscle. Both sprains and strains usually heal without surgery.

関節包

挫傷

An ankle sprain, or sprained ankle, is the most common

ligament injury. It often occurs when the foot twists during plantar flexion and body weight is concentrated on the outside step at the same time. This puts great force on the ankle.

足底屈（足底方向に屈折すること）

Ankle sprains are common among people who are active in sports such as football, basketball, running, and so forth, but they also commonly occur in the course of routine daily activities like going up or down stairs and even just taking a walk. Ankle sprains cause localized pain (usually tenderness on the outer side of the ankle), swelling, black-and-blue discoloration at the site of the injury, and loss of mobility.

圧痛

Ankle sprains are classified into the following 3 categories, according to the extent of damage to the ligaments:

Grade I: an injury without macroscopic tears or instability; mild pain and tenderness are present.

1度

Grade II: a partial tear with mild to moderate joint instability; moderate pain and tenderness are present.

Grade III: a complete tear with inability to bear weight, and joint instability; severe pain, tenderness, occasional internal bleeding, and swelling are present, and the joint capsule is torn.

Treatment

Treatment depends on the severity of the ligament injury, but immediate elevation and rest of the ankle are always advisable. When no fractures or injury to the ligaments are diagnosed, the best treatment is rest, ice, compression, and elevation (RICE). For grade I and II sprains, in addition to RICE, a cold compress should be applied to the ankle to reduce swelling. For grade II and III sprains, the ankle is preferably immobilized with braces for two or three weeks to limit inversion/eversion stress.

挙上

圧迫

If the injury does not heal properly, or a ligament rupture occurs, the best treatment is to fix the ankle with a plaster cast for three to six weeks and to carry out surgery after the cast is removed.

☆ これだけは覚えておきたい英語

- · **bandage** 包帯
- · **compression** 圧迫
- · **immobilizer** 固定器具
- · **splint** 副子
- · **brace** 装具
- · **dislocation** 脱臼
- · **sling** 三角巾

ことばのルーツ

- **sprain**　**捻挫：**フランス語espraindre（回転する）から。
- **patella**　**膝蓋骨：**不確かであるが，ラテン語で「平たい容器」の意味。
- **quadriceps femoris**　**大腿四頭筋：**quadri-はラテン語で4，cepsはラテン語で頭（caput）の意味。
- **meniscus**　**半月板：**ギリシャ語mene（moon：月）＋cresco（crescent：成長する）。

Therapeutic Exercises for Sports Injuries
スポーツ傷害の運動療法

（イラストは柳澤　健（編）：イラスト理学療法ブラウン・ノート．メジカルビュー社，2007より引用）

アイスマッサージ

Ice massage

ジャンパー膝やシンスプリントなど，炎症反応の強い急性期にはアイスマッサージを行う。

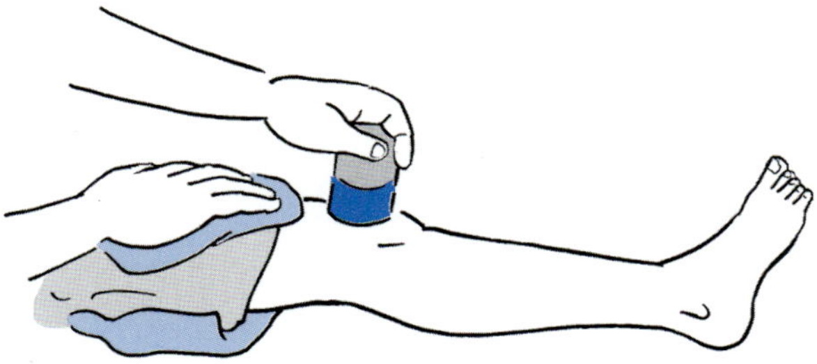

Instructions to the patient

Your knee is a bit inflamed, but an ice massage should reduce the pain. Just try gently rubbing the parts that hurt with this ice for 10 minutes or so.

あなたの膝は炎症が原因で痛んでいます。アイスマッサージが痛みを和らげるでしょう。アイスを膝の痛む箇所に置いて10分間ゆっくり動かしてください。

ハムストリングスのストレッチング

Hamstring stretch to increase flexibility

ハムストリングスの柔軟性を高めるためにストレッチングを行う。

Instructions to the patient

I'm going to lift your leg, keeping it straight. OK, let's hold it there for 30 seconds. Good. Now the other one. This exercise will make the muscles in the back of your thighs more flexible and help prevent hamstring injuries.

私があなたの脚をまっすぐ上げて伸ばします。これを30秒間保ちます。次は反対の脚も同じようにします。この運動は太もも裏の筋肉を柔軟にし，損傷を予防します。

チューブを用いた運動療法

Using elastic bands to strengthen the hamstrings

チューブを用いて下腿遠位部に抵抗を加える。

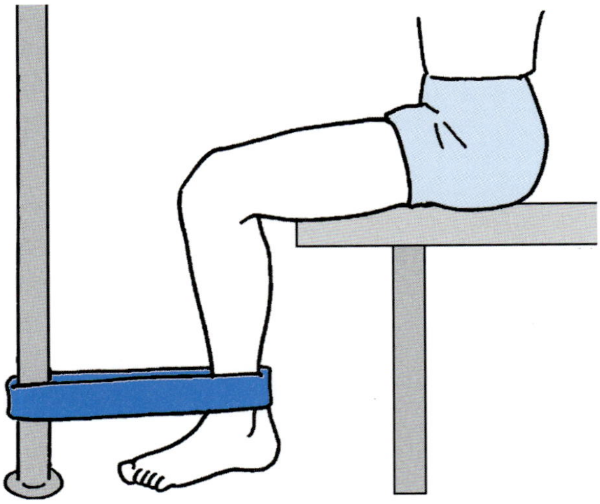

Instructions to the patient

Sit on the chair facing the pole. Now put one foot in the elastic band and pull it toward yourself. This exercise strengthens the muscles in the back of your thighs.

イスに座って柱にかけたチューブの一方に足を入れて引っ張ります。これは太もも裏の筋肉を鍛える運動です。

重錘バンドを用いた運動療法

Using ankle weights to strengthen the hamstrings

足首に重錘を用いて下腿遠位部に軽い抵抗を加える。

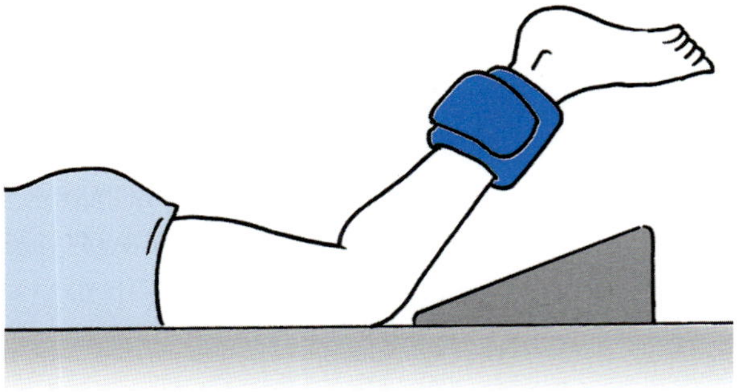

Instructions to the patient

If you'd like to lie on your stomach, I'll put a weight on each of your ankles to provide some resistance. Now keep your knees on the floor, and starting with your left leg, raise and lower it slowly 10 times. Now, do the same thing with your right leg.

うつぶせになってください。左足首に重錘をつけます。そこから，ゆっくりと膝を曲げ，ゆっくりと戻してください。それを10回繰り返します。反対の足首も同じことをします。

大腿四頭筋のストレッチング

Quadriceps stretching

大腿四頭筋(特に大腿直筋)のストレッチングを行う。

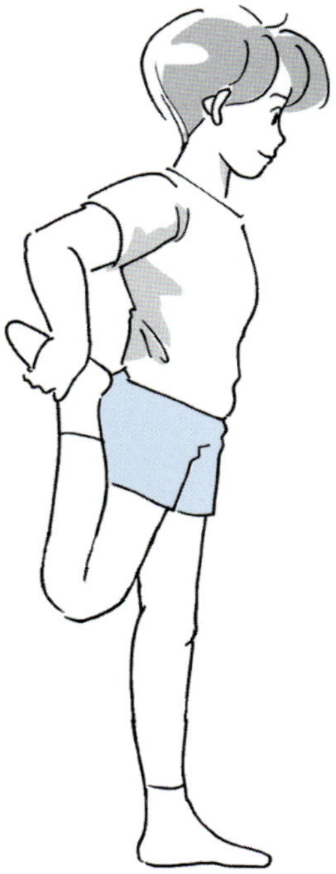

Instructions to the patient

First of all, I'd like you to stand on one leg. Now take the other leg and pull it up toward your back. This is a good stretching exercise for your thighs.

まず片脚で立ってください。もう一方の脚を背中のほうへ引っ張りあげてください。これは大腿のよいストレッチング運動です。

腓骨筋群の筋力強化

Stretching for peroneus muscles to prevent sprain of the ankle joint

足関節捻挫を予防するために腓骨筋群を強化する。

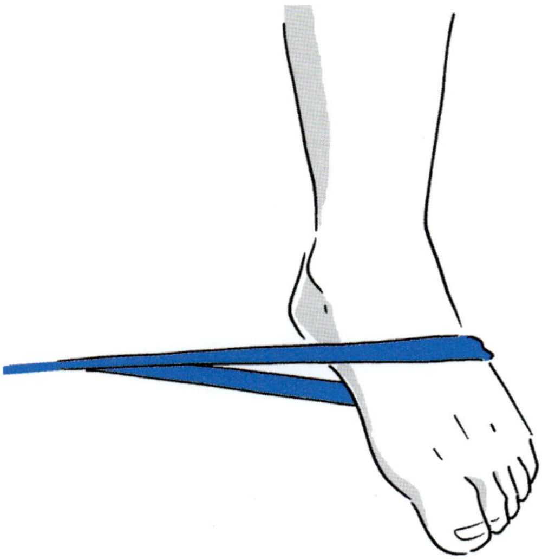

Instructions to the patient

Put your foot inside the loop for me. OK, now using just your foot, I want you to try to stretch the loop out to the side as far as you can. Don't move your leg. OK, relax. Now, do it another 9 t mes.

チューブに足を入れて外側に引っ張ってください。次に緩めてください。この運動を10回繰り返します。

INTRODUCTION
CHAPTER I
CHAPTER II
CHAPTER III
CHAPTER IV
APPENDIX

One-point Lesson

Common sports injuries	一般的なスポーツ傷害
anterior cruciate ligament injury	前十字靱帯損傷
Achilles tendon rupture	アキレス腱断裂
Achilles tendonitis	アキレス腱炎
concussion	脳しんとう
dislocated shoulder	肩関節脱臼
golfer's elbow (medial epicondylitis)	ゴルフ肘（内側上顆炎）
groin pull, strain, or tear	鼠径部損傷／捻挫／裂傷
heel spurs (bone spurs)	踵骨棘
meniscus injury	半月板損傷
little league elbow (medial epicondylitis)	リトルリーグ肘（内側上顆炎）
plantar fasciitis	足底筋膜炎
runner's knee (chondromalacia patellae)	ランナー膝（膝蓋軟骨軟化症）
Sever's disease (calcaneal apophysitis)	シーバー病（踵骨骨端炎）
shin splints	シンスプリント（脛骨過労性骨膜炎）
sprained ankle	足関節捻挫
tennis elbow (lateral epicondylitis)	テニス肘（外側上顆炎）
torn rotator cuff	回旋筋腱板裂傷

EXERCISES

1. RICEの各アルファベットが表す英語を書きなさい。

(1) R________________ (2) I________________

(3) C________________ (4) E________________

2. 不要なアルファベットを除き，英単語を見つけなさい。

b e l i n j u r y o v r u p t u r e o m s p r a i n u p t e n d o n o v t r a c t i o n

(1)________________ (2)________________ (3)________________

(4)________________ (5)________________

3. (1)～(5)の英語の説明に該当するものをa～eから選びなさい。

(1) dislocation ( ) (2) injury ( ) (3) rupture ( )

(4) sprain ( ) (5) strain ( )

a. a condition where a body organ or membrane bursts or breaks

b. a condition where a muscle has been overstretched or torn owing to a strong or sudden movement

c. a condition where the ligaments in a joint have been overstretched or torn due to a sudden twist

d. a general word to describe any damage or wound to a person's body such as that caused by an accident

e. displacement of a bone from its normal position at a joint

4. 内容が正しい文にはTを，間違っている文にはFを記入しなさい。

(1) _____ Patients with Achilles tendon rupture should be treated only by using orthosis without undergoing rehabilitation.

(2) _____ Reduction is the second best treatment for a dislocated shoulder.

(3) _____ Dislocated shoulders are rare in people who are active in contact sports.

(4) _____ When no fractures or injuries to the ligaments are diagnosed, the best treatment is not limited to RICE.

(5) _____ If an injury does not heal properly, surgery should be performed as soon as possible.

Spinal Cord Injury 脊髄損傷

脊髄損傷は，脳と体をつなぐ脊髄が脱臼や骨折などの外傷を受けた際に生じる。また，脊柱管の狭い部位に外傷が加わる，あるいはヘルニアや腫瘍によって脊髄が圧迫されると損傷が起きる。損傷の程度によって，脊髄が横に離断し，神経伝達機能が完全に絶たれた状態の「完全型」と，脊髄の一部機能が残存する「不完全型」に分かれる。「完全型」の場合，脳からの情報が正確に伝わらなくなるため，運動機能，感覚知覚機能が失われ，自律神経も著しく障害される。急性期を過ぎると褥創（じょくそう）や尿路感染症，排尿障害，排便障害，起立性低血圧，肺炎，下肢静脈血栓症，拘縮（関節が硬くなる）などの合併症が生じる。

脊髄損傷では，患者がまず現実を直視し，障害をもったまま生きるという「障害受容」が重要な課題となる。したがって，リハビリテーションの目的は，機能回復ではなく，残された機能を最大限に使って，日常生活動作（activities of daily living: ADL）を可能にすることにある。そのためには，呼吸訓練，プッシュアップ動作，長座位訓練，筋力強化，車椅子の操作などに習熟することが求められる。

現在日本には10万人以上の脊髄損傷者がおり，その原因の多くは，交通事故，高所からの落下であり，最近はスポーツによるものも増えている。

Definition

Spinal cord injuries — damage to any part of the spinal cord or nerves at the end of the spinal canal — often cause permanent changes in strength, sensation, and other body functions below the site of the injury. If you've recently experienced a spinal cord injury, it might seem as if every aspect of your life will be affected.

Many scientists are optimistic that advances in research will someday make the repair of spinal cord injuries possible. Research studies are ongoing around the world. In the meantime, treatment and rehabilitation allow many people with spinal cord injuries to lead productive, independent lives.

spinal canal: 脊椎管
optimistic: 楽観的 ⇔ pessimistic
repair: 修復

Symptoms

Your ability to control your limbs after a spinal cord injury depends on two factors: the location of the injury along your spinal cord and the severity of the injury. The lowest part of the spinal cord that functions normally after injury is known as the neurological level of the injury. The severity of the injury is often referred to in terms of "completeness" and is classified as either of the following:

severity: 重症度

- Complete. If almost all feeling (sensation) and all ability to control movement (motor function) are lost below the spinal cord injury, the injury is complete. 完全
- Incomplete. If there is some motor or sensory function below the affected area, the injury is incomplete. There are varying degrees of incomplete injury. 不全

Additionally, paralysis resulting from a spinal cord injury may be referred to as: 麻痺

- Tetraplegia. Also known as quadriplegia, this means your arms, hands, trunk, legs, and pelvic organs are all affected by your spinal cord injury. 四肢麻痺＝quadriplegia
- Paraplegia. The paralysis affects all or part of the trunk, legs and pelvic organs. 対麻痺

(Reproduced with modification from "http://www.mayoclinic.org/diseases-conditions/spinal-cord-injury/basics/symptoms/con-20023837")

Notes

❶ **spinal canal = vertebral canal　脊椎管**：脊髄，脊髄膜，および関連組織を入れる管。関節により結合した一連の椎骨の追行によって作られる。

❷ **repair　修復**：傷害された組織に一連の反応が起こり，その形態と機能が部分的に回復すること。

ことばのルーツ

数字を表す接頭辞

接頭辞（prefix）は，語の前に付き語の意味や文法上の変化をもたらす。例えば，tetraplegia，quadriplegiaは，-plegia（「麻痺」の意の連結形）と4を表すギリシャ語由来の接頭辞tetra-，ラテン語由来のquadri-が付けられた用語である。以下に10までの数字を表す接頭辞を列挙する（前者がギリシャ語，後者がラテン語）。接頭辞のつく医学英語を辞書で探すのも面白いであろう。月並みな言い方だが「たかが数字，されど数字」である。

hemi-/semi-	1/2	**pent-/quinque**	5	**deca-/deci-**	10
mono-/uni-	1	**hex-/sex-**	6		
di-/bi-	2	**hepta-/sept-**	7		
tri-/ter-	3	**octa-/octo-**	8		
tetr-/quadri-	4	**ennea-/nona-, novem-**	9		

注：ちなみにparaplegiaのpara- は場所を，substantia nigraのsub-は方向を表す接頭辞である。また，plagia-のような連結形は語根から作られて，語に似た意味をもつが独立して用いられない。この連結形を多く覚えることは，リハビリテーション分野でも用いられる医学英語に強くなる早道であるといえる。

One-point Lesson

脊椎の位置別完全損傷による障害

Cervical level　頸椎レベル

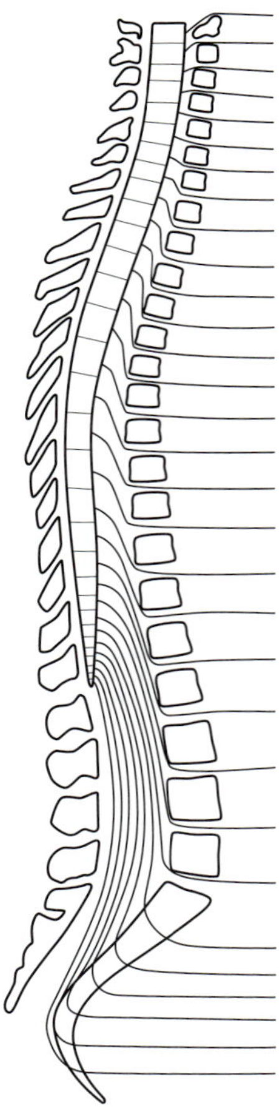

C1–C3：横隔膜を含む呼吸筋収縮不能。事故時にほとんどが死亡するが，生存の場合は入院，生涯人工呼吸器の助けを必要とし，気管切開術の必要性が高い。

C1：感覚と動きは顔に限定される。

C2：後頭部の頭皮にも感覚がある（C1，C2ともに首が頭部を支持できず，直座は外科的安定化あるいは外的安定化を必要とする）。

C3：頭部，頸部の感覚および頸部筋肉のコントロールが可能。

C4：主として人工呼吸器を必要とし，横隔膜の機能は残存する。その結果，自発呼吸が再び可能となる。C4損傷者は肩を上げる筋肉が機能するが，下げる筋肉は動かない。

C5：上腕の運動はできるが，手のコントロールは不可能。C4損傷者よりも横隔膜が機能する。通常，肩の機能は維持され，肘は柔軟に動く。

C6：手を少し動かすことが可能で，上腕，親指，示指に感覚がある。手を支持するために手首の装具が必要。

C7：腕と手を多少動かすことができる。より上腕のコントロールができるので，肘をまっすぐに伸ばすことができる。通常，肩と肘の動きは正常であるが，手の開きは半分程度である。腕，親指，示指，中指，環指の一部に感覚がある。

C8：手をより動かすことができ，感覚がある。しかし繊細な手の動きはできない。母指とほか四指をよく動かすことができるので，物を拾ったり持ったりできる。

Upper thoracic level　上部胸椎レベル

T1：手と腕をよくコントロールできる。T1および以下の脊椎の損傷者は，四肢麻痺よりも対麻痺とみなされる。腕，手すべてに感覚がある。

T2–T5：上部胸椎レベルの損傷は，手，脚部に障害はないが，呼吸にいくらかの障害が残る。より下位の損傷は，呼吸には比較的問題を生じないが，咳は困難である。

Lower thoracic level　下部胸椎レベル

T6–T12：胸部下位損傷は，呼吸はうまくできるが，腹筋に障害がある。咳は腹筋によるが，T9以下の損傷では可能。

Lumbar (L) and Sacral (S) levels　腰椎・仙椎レベル

腰椎・仙椎における損傷は，損傷レベルによって感覚の量と脚部のコントロールに違いがある。

L1–L5：排便と膀胱機能に障害があるが，反射排尿は可能。

S1–S5：歩行は可能であるが，介助が必要。排便・膀胱機能はなお障害がある。

Therapeutic Exercises for Spinal Cord Injuries
脊髄損傷の運動療法

上腕二頭筋の収縮練習

Strengthening exercise for the biceps

患者自身が，前腕（と手）を持ち上げながら上腕二頭筋を収縮させる。

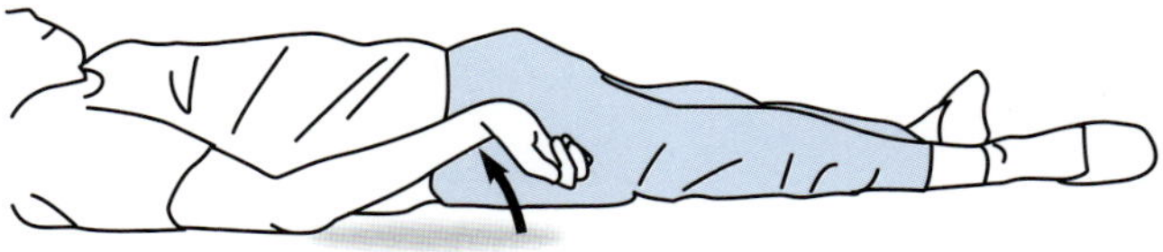

Instructions to the patient

Lie on your back. Keeping your elbows on the floor, raise your hands slowly and pay attention to how heavy they feel.

仰向けに寝てください。
上腕を床につけたままで，前腕をその重さを感じながらゆっくりと上げてください。

プッシュアップ動作訓練

Push-ups in a wheelchair

手掌を車椅子のアームサポートに置き，上肢と体幹を床面と直立させた状態で持ち上げる。

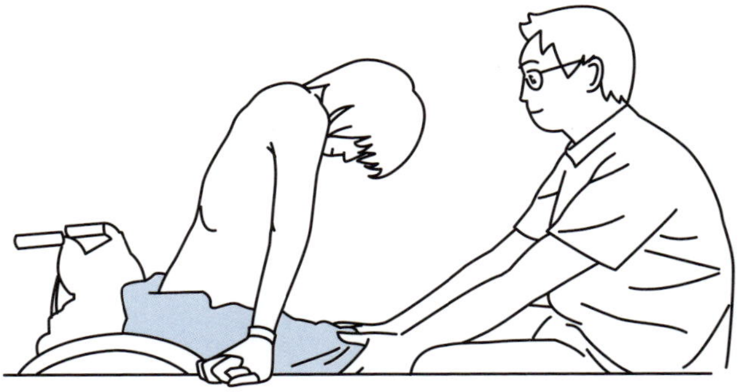

Instructions to the patient

Let's try some wheelchair push-ups. First, place your hands on the armrests and push down. Try to lift your buttocks off the seat. I'll hold your legs to keep you from falling forward.

プッシュアップ動作の訓練をしましょう。手を車椅子のアームサポートに置き，下に押し，お尻を持ち上げてください。体が前に傾かないように，私が脚を押さえています。

EXERCISES

1. 不要なアルファベットを除き，英単語を見つけなさい。

ordswellingvixinfectionsorylesioncomspinal

(1) ______________________ (2) ______________________

(3) ______________________ (4) ______________________

2. 脊髄の部位を示す略語の完全形を書きなさい。

(1) C______________________ (2) T______________________

(3) L______________________ (4) S______________________

3. 内容が正しい文にはTを，間違っている文にはFを記入しなさい。

(1) _____ A spinal cord injury is defined as damage to any part of the spinal column or nerves at the end of the spinal canal.

(2) _____ Rehabilitation will not help patients with spinal cord injuries to lead productive and independent lives until it is possible to repair such injuries.

(3) _____ The extent to which patients can control their limbs after spinal cord injury depends only on the location of the injury along the spinal cord.

(4) _____ The lowest part of the spinal cord that functions normally after injury is referred to as the neurological level of the injury.

(5) _____ If most or all feeling and ability to control movement are lost below the spinal cord injury, the injury is called incomplete.

Parkinson's Disease　パーキンソン病

パーキンソン病は，発見者であるイギリスの医師，James Parkinson（1755～1824）にちなんだ病名である。振せん麻痺（parkinsonism）ともいい，手足の震え（tremor），体の筋肉の硬化（固縮：rigidity）および随意運動の硬直（無動：akinesia），そして前傾姿勢（姿勢保持障害：disorder of posture）の徴候がみられる。発病年齢は50歳代からが最も多く，中高年の病気であるが，病因は脳幹部基底神経節の黒質に損傷が生じることで（原因不明），運動動作を円滑にする線条体に情報を送るドパミン（dopamine）が減少し，アセチルコリン（acetylcholine）が増加する。結果的に動作，運動に障害が生じる。

BACKGROUND INFORMATION

Parkinson's disease (PD) is a chronic and progressive movement disorder, meaning that symptoms continue and worsen over time. Nearly one million people in the US are living with PD. The cause is unknown, and although there is presently no cure, there are treatment options such as medication and surgery to manage its symptoms.

進行性運動障害

PD involves the malfunction and death of vital nerve cells in the brain, called neurons. PD primarily affects neurons in an area of the brain called the substantia nigra. Some of these dying neurons produce dopamine, a chemical that sends messages to the part of the brain that controls movement and coordination. As the disease progresses, the amount of dopamine produced in the brain decreases, leaving a person unable to control movement normally.

機能不全

黒質

ドパミン

The specific group of symptoms that an individual experiences varies from person to person. Primary motor signs of PD include the following:

- tremor of the hands, arms, legs, jaw, and face
- bradykinesia (slowness of movement)
- rigidity or stiffness of the limbs and trunk
- postural instability or impaired balance and coordination

個人（集団の一員としての）

振せん

運動緩徐

固縮，硬直

姿勢不安定／バランス・調和運動障害

Common Treatment and Medication

There are many medications available to treat the symptoms of PD, although none yet that actually reverse the effects of the

INTRODUCTION　CHAPTER I　CHAPTER II　CHAPTER III　CHAPTER IV　APPENDIX

disease. It is common for people with PD to take a variety of these medications – all at different doses and at different times of day – in order to manage the symptoms of the disease.

(Reproduced with modification from "http://www.pdf.org/en/about_pd")

薬の服用量（の1回分）

Notes

❶ **substantia nigra**　**黒質**：substantia（質）＋nigra（黒）。色彩を表す語については，下記「ことばのルーツ」を参照。

❷ **dopamine (DM)** [dóupəmìːn]　**ドパミン**：中枢神経中にあり，神経伝達物質として作用する。生体内およびチロシンから合成される，ノルアドレナリン（ノルエピネフリン）とアドレナリン（エピネフリン）の前駆物質。ドパミンの欠乏によりパーキンソン病を起こす。

☆ これだけは覚えておきたい英語

• **bradykinesia**	運動緩徐	• **dose**	投与量
• **impaired coordination**	調和運動障害	• **rigidity**	固縮
• **substantia nigra**	黒質	• **tremor**	振せん

ことばのルーツ

色彩語を含む医学英語

英文中のthe substantia nigraのnigraは，ラテン語で黒を意味するnigerがsubstantiaを修飾する形容詞nigraとなったものである。白質(albus)はthe substantia alba。灰質はcinerea，灰白質はgrisea，鉄色素はferrugineaがそれぞれsubstantiaに後置する。

ほかにも医学英語にはギリシャ語の色彩語からつくられた用語がある。

leukos（白）	→ leuk-	→ leukocyte（白血球）
erythros（赤）	→ erythr-	→ erythrocyte（赤血球）
melas（黒）	→ melan-	→ melanoblast（メラニン芽細胞）
polios（灰）	→ polio-	→ poliomyelitis（灰白髄炎）
kirrhosis（黄褐色）	→ cirrh-	→ cirrhosis（黄疸）
xanthos（黄）	→ xanth-	→ xanthoma（黄色腫）
kyanos（青）	→ cyan-	→ cyanosis（チアノーゼ）
chloros（緑）	→ chlor-	→ chloroform（クロロフォルム）など

Therapeutic Exercises for Parkinson's Disease
パーキンソン病の運動療法

（イラストは柳澤　健（編）：イラスト理学療法ブラウン・ノート．メジカルビュー社，2007より引用）

自転車エルゴメーター（ヤールの重症度分類ステージⅠ～Ⅲ）

Pedaling a cycle ergometer (Hoehn-Yahr grading stages I – III)

自転車エルゴメーターをこぐ。

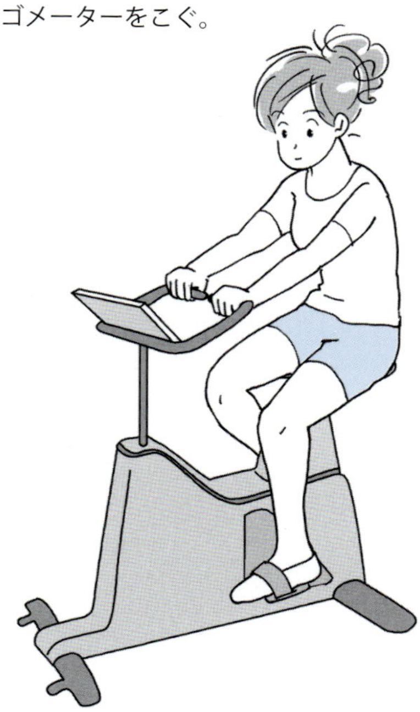

Instructions to the patient

Sit on the exercise bike. Now hold the handlebars and pedal slowly.

自転車エルゴメーターに座ってください。ハンドルをもってペダルをゆっくりこいでください。

階段昇降練習（ヤールの重症度分類ステージⅢ）

Climbing up stairs (Hoehn-Yahr grading stage III)

階段の昇降練習を行う。

Instructions to the patient

Let's try climbing the stairs. Take your time. It'll be easier if you hold the handrail.

階段を上がりましょう。急ぐ必要はありません。手すりを（片手で）持つと楽になるでしょう。

手拍子に合わせた歩行（ヤールの重症度分類ステージⅢ）

Gait training to hand-clapping (Hoehn-Yahr grading stage III)

手拍子に合わせて歩く。

Instructions to the patient

I'm going to clap my hands, and I'd like you to walk to the rhythm. This exercise will help you walk more smoothly.

私が手を叩きます。リズムに合わせて歩きましょう。これは円滑な歩き方を取り戻す練習です。

柔軟体操（ヤールの重症度分類ステージⅢ～Ⅳ）

Flexibility exercise: side flexion of the trunk in sitting (Hoehn-Yahr grading stages III–IV)

柔軟体操（座位姿勢での側屈）を行う。

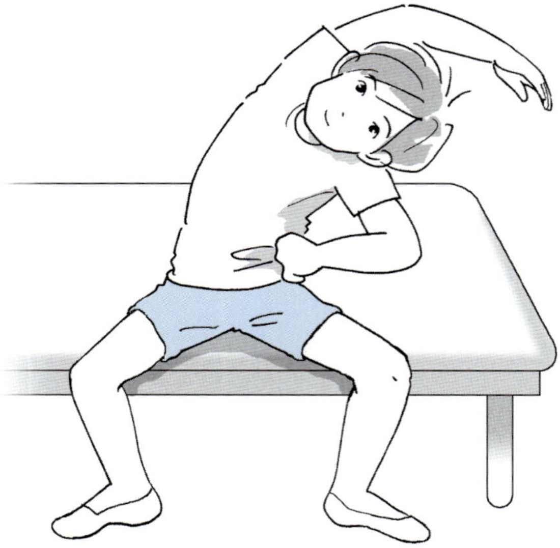

Instructions to the patient

I'd like you to sit on the edge of the bed and put your left hand on your waist. Please lean your body to the left. Now, do the same thing on the other side.

ベッドの端に座ります。片手を腰にあてて体を楽な範囲で横に倒してください。反対側で同じ動作をします。

EXERCISES

1. 日本語に相当する英語を書きなさい。

(1) ウイルス ______________________

(2) 運動緩徐 ______________________

(3) 機能不全 ______________________

(4) 固縮 ______________________

(5) 振せん ______________________

2. 正しい語を囲みなさい。

(1) Parkinson's disease is (an acute/a chronic) disease.

(2) Parkinson's disease is a (progressive/regressive) disease.

(3) Parkinson's disease attacks the brain's (substantia alba/substantia nigra).

(4) Parkinson's disease affects (movement/thinking).

(5) There are (various medications/no medications) that are effective in reversing the damage caused by Parkinson's disease.

Stroke　脳卒中

脳のエネルギー源である酸素と栄養素は，左右2本の内頸動脈と椎骨動脈から送られて，脳全体に枝分かれした動脈によって脳実質にいきわたる。脳卒中はそれらの血管に損傷が生じ，生命の危険にさらされる状態をいう。血管が破れたり詰まったりするのは，心臓疾患，高血圧，糖尿病，脳の動脈瘤などに起因し，脳卒中を防ぐには，まず生活レベルでの注意が必要である。

脳卒中の発生は，出血と梗塞に分類され，治療では薬物療法と併せて後遺症の運動・言語障害と廃用症候群を克服するための訓練（医学的リハビリテーション）が不可欠である。

BACKGROUND INFORMATION

A stroke is an interruption in the blood flow to parts of the brain, and it often results in brain injury. A stroke only lasts for a few minutes, but the symptoms the injury to the brain causes are often permanent. As with other brain injuries, the specific symptoms depend on the areas of the brain affected by the stroke.

脳卒中《一般用語》＝cerebrovascular accident（CVA）脳血管障害。strokeは脳血流障害に関連して起きるすべての急性，臨床的出来事を指す。

A wide range of symptoms are observed, including sensory, coordination, and motor problems, language and cognitive difficulties, and personality changes. However, the areas of the brain controlling motor activity are the ones most commonly affected, so physical problems are more common than cognitive ones. In the months after a stroke, a person will usually experience a spontaneous return of at least some functional ability. Different types of rehabilitation therapy can further improve functional abilities. However, significant, permanent losses are also involved.

感覚の

認知障害

人格変容

自発的回復

Two types of stroke　脳卒中2つのタイプ

(1) Ischemic stroke（虚血性脳卒中）

Ischemic strokes❶ are the more common of the two types of stroke, and are usually less severe. During an ischemic stroke, a blockage in a blood vessel prevents blood from reaching parts of the brain, and cells in those parts of the brain die. This is usually caused by atherosclerosis,❷ which makes the blood vessels narrower. There are two types of ischemic stroke, thrombotic

アテローム硬化症

and embolic. Thrombotic strokes are more common: a blood clot (or thrombus) forms on top of plaque deposited on the inner walls of a blood vessel, which contributes to the narrowing of the blood vessel, blocking blood flow and resulting in a thrombotic stroke. In an embolic stroke, a clot forms in a blood vessel, becomes detached and floats through the circulatory system as an embolus until it lodges in a narrow blood vessel, blocking the flow of blood. Both thrombotic and embolic strokes❸ have the same result: tissue death caused by a lack of nutrients and oxygen; only the source of the clot is different.

血餅／血栓

塞栓

血栓性／
塞栓性〔脳〕卒中

(2) Hemorrhagic stroke（出血性脳卒中）

A hemorrhagic stroke is caused by a rupture in the wall of a blood vessel, which allows blood to flow directly into the tissues. Strange as it may seem, blood is toxic to cells, and direct contact with it can permanently damage brain tissue. The break in the artery wall is usually caused by the rupture of an aneurysm — a sort of ballooning out of part of the artery wall that is often associated with atherosclerosis, although it can have other causes.

破裂

動脈壁／動脈瘤

Besides the damage caused by contact with the blood, two other factors permanently damage brain tissue during a hemorrhagic stroke. One is the lack of fresh oxygen and nutrients because of the interruption in blood flow. The other is the build up of pressure inside the brain. In a hemorrhagic stroke, the increased fluid only makes the condition worse by squeezing the brain cells harder. Hemorrhagic strokes result in a greater loss of functional ability than ischemic strokes; however, hemorrhagic strokes are much less common.

Common Treatment and Medication

Although there are many medical procedures involved in critical care for a stroke, long-term care focuses almost entirely on the consequences of any brain injury caused by the stroke. Treatment of the brain injury depends, in turn, on the specific features of the injury and its functional consequences for the individual.

医学的処置

Once an individual has a stroke, that individual is at a higher risk of additional strokes. Thus, the individual should take medicine to control risk factors such as high blood pressure, diabetes, and atherosclerosis.

高血圧

糖尿病

(Reproduced [with modifications] with permission from Handbook of Disabilities by RCEP at the University of Missouri.)

Notes

❶**ischemic stroke 虚血性脳卒中**：ischemia（ischo-「中断」＋haima「血液」)→ischemic（形容詞）

❷**atherosclerosis　アテローム〔性動脈〕硬化症**：大動脈，中動脈にコレステロールが沈着し，動脈壁が狭くなり，最終的に斑が線維化・石灰化し，血流障害を起こすと梗塞の危険性を生じる。athero-（ドイツ語，Atherom「粉瘤」→粥状）＋sclero-（ギリシャ語「硬い」）＋-osis（接尾辞「状態」）

❸**thrombotic stroke　血栓性脳卒中**：thrombusはギリシャ語thrombos（血液凝固）から。心血管系の凝塊で閉塞性。また血管壁や心臓壁に付着することもある。

❹**hemiparesis 片側不全麻痺**：hemi-（接頭辞「半分」）＋par-（接頭辞「両側」）＋-esis（接尾辞「状態」)。おそらくhemiparalysis（両側の半分が麻痺した状態）の省略形。

❺**paralysis 完全麻痺**：para-（片方が緩む）＋lysis（分解）

❻**aphasia 失語症**：a-（接頭辞「欠乏，無」）＋phasis（言語能力）＋-ia（接尾辞「病的状態」)。alogia，apraxiaのa-も同じ意味の接頭辞。

［注］❹❺❻は次頁のOne-point Lessonを参照。

☆ これだけは覚えておきたい英語

• **stroke**	脳卒中
• **atherosclerosis**	アテローム〔性動脈〕硬化症
• **thrombus**	血栓
• **embolus**	塞栓
• **hemorrhagic**	出血性（< hemorrhage　出血）
• **aneurysm**	動脈瘤

One-point Lesson

Main symptoms of a stroke　脳卒中の顕著な症状

脳卒中が影響を及ぼした脳の部位が，身体のどこに機能障害を起こすかを決定する。
以下のようなよくみられる症状に適したリハビリテーションが行われる。

(1) physical symptoms　身体の症状

- weakness of one arm or leg　片側の腕/脚の脆弱
- hemiparesis[4] on one side of the body　身体の半側不全麻痺
- paralysis[5] of one arm or leg, or on one side of the body　片側の腕/脚，身体の半側の全麻痺
- loss of part of the visual field in both eyes　両眼視覚野の部分的喪失

(2) language disorders　言語の障害

- difficulty speaking intelligibly or understanding the speech of others　明瞭な発話困難あるいは他者の言語の理解困難
- aphasia[6]　失語症，alogia　会話不能：全般的な言語機能（話す，聞く，書く，読む）が損なわれた状態。motor aphasia（運動性失語症；主に話しことばと書くことが損なわれ，ことばの理解は保たれている），sensory aphasia（感覚性失語症；ことばの理解，話しことばの異常に気がつかない状態）
- dysarthria　構音（構語）障害：会話に用いる構音筋（舌，唇，咽頭，喉頭）の麻痺，失調，けいれんなどによって発語が不明瞭になった状態。

(3) mental disorders　精神的障害

- sleep disorder　睡眠障害
- depression　うつ

(4) apraxia (mild cases)　失行症（軽症）

- reduced short-term memory　短期記憶減退
- difficulty in writing or calculating　書字・計算困難
- confusion of left and right　左・右混同
- difficulty in concentrating　集中困難

Daily Activities for Patients with Hemiplegia
片麻痺の患者の日常動作

（イラストは柳澤　健（編）：イラスト理学療法ブラウン・ノート．メジカルビュー社，2007より引用）

健側からの起き上がり

Getting up from the unaffected side

健側を下にして起き上がる。

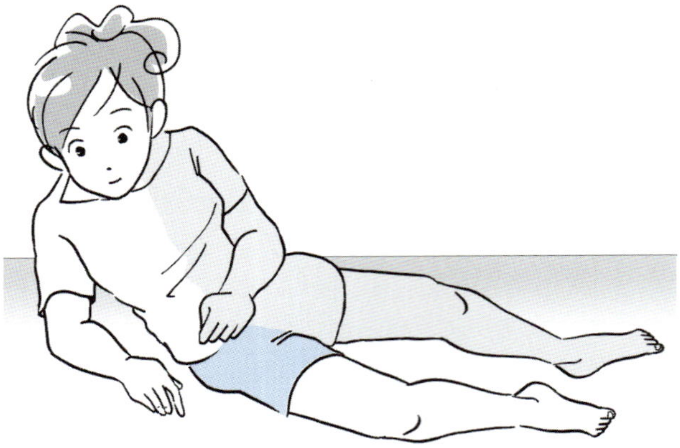

Instructions to the patient

First, turn your head toward the unaffected side. Now support your body with your unaffected arm and try to push yourself up.

まず，麻痺のない側に頭を向けてください。次に腕で体を支えながら起こします。

階段を昇る

Climbing stairs

階段や段差を昇る場合には，まず①杖を上段について，次に②健側下肢を挙げ，最後に③患側下肢をのせる。

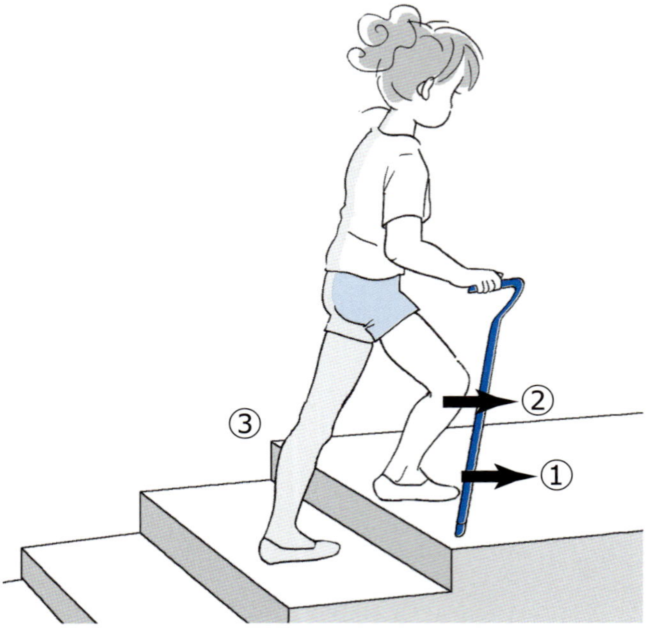

Instructions to the patient

When you're going up the stairs, you should always first place your cane on the next step up. Then lead with your unaffected leg and move up to the next step.

階段を上がるときは，まず杖を上段に置きます。麻痺のない足から先に階段を登ります。

歩行練習

Gait training

理学療法士と一緒に歩行練習をする。

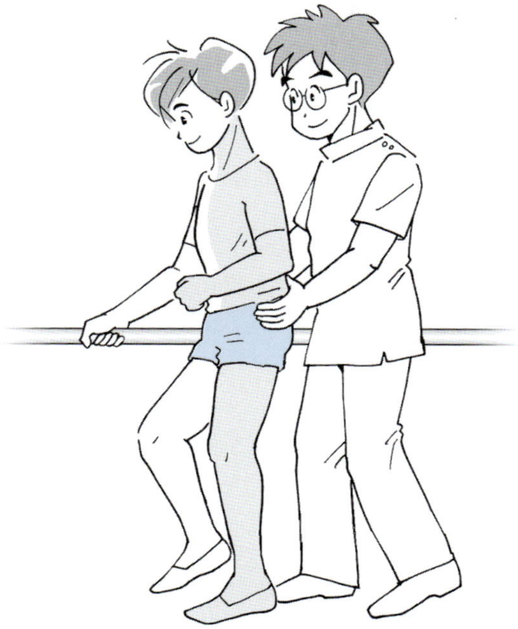

Instructions to the patient

Let's try some walking training. Take your time. I'm going to hold your hips to help you keep your balance. Use the handrail if you need to.

歩行練習をしましょう。急がなくていいですよ。私があなたの腰を支えます。必要なら手すりを持ってください。

短下肢装具をつけての歩行練習

Gait training with an ankle-foot orthosis

短下肢装具をつけて歩行練習をする。

Instructions to the patient

Let's try some walking training with a short leg brace. This will help you to walk more smoothly.

短下肢装具をつけて歩行訓練を始めましょう。この装具はスムースに歩くのを助けます。

足関節背屈運動の促通（ステージⅢ）

Facilitation of ankle dorsiflexion (Brunnstrom Approach, stage III)

ステージⅢに対し，股関節屈曲筋群の抵抗運動を行う。

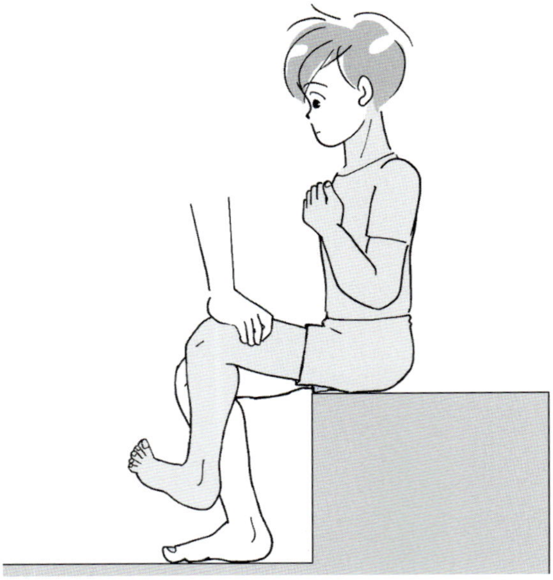

Instructions to the patient

Try to raise your foot off the ground as I press down on your knee. This will improve the strength of your hip flexors.

私が膝を押さえている間，足を上げてください。この運動は股関節の筋強化に効果的です。

EXERCISES

1. 英語に相当する日本語を選びなさい。

(1) aneurysm	(　　)	a. 塞栓
(2) embolus	(　　)	b. 血栓
(3) hemorrhagic stroke	(　　)	c. 動脈瘤
(4) ischemic stroke	(　　)	d. 虚血性卒中
(5) thrombus	(　　)	e. 出血性卒中

2. 英文がischemic strokeを説明するものにはa，hemorrhagic strokeにはbを書きなさい。

(1) Accumulated blood strongly compresses the brain cells. (　　)

(2) An enlarged artery in the brain ruptures and damages the surrounding tissue. (　　)

(3) Emboli block blood vessels and cut off the flow of fresh oxygen and nutrients to the brain. (　　)

(4) This kind of stroke is and less severe. (　　)

(5) This kind of stroke is much less common. (　　)

Chronic Obstructive Pulmonary Disease (COPD)
慢性閉塞性肺疾患

　気管支を侵す慢性気管支炎（chronic bronchitis）と，ガス交換が行われる肺胞に病変をきたす肺気腫（emphysema）の総称を慢性閉塞性肺疾患（COPD）という。病因の1つは長期の喫煙と考えられ，高齢男性の死因の高位を占めている。進行した段階では，呼吸不全を引き起こし，生命を危うくする場合もある。病状が安定している場合の治療は「禁煙」「気管支拡張薬，ステロイド薬の薬物治療」「適切な運動などのリハビリテーション」である。

BACKGROUND INFORMATION

Chronic obstructive pulmonary disease (COPD)[1] is a group of lung diseases that make it very difficult to breathe. It is progressive and potentially life threatening, but not contagious.

接触感染性の

The term "obstructive" means that the person is not able to exhale well, which leaves "old" air in the lungs and reduces the amount of "new" (oxygenated) air the person can bring in with the next breath.

There is growing evidence that COPD is the result of long-term (often decades-long) inflammation caused by breathing in irritating smoke, dust particles, or fumes. Smoking cigarettes is the most common cause of COPD, but there are possible genetic factors that make some people who smoke more likely to develop COPD than others. Prolonged exposure to other lung irritants such as chemicals or industrial dust can also cause COPD.

刺激性噴煙／粉塵／煙霧

長期にわたる曝露

The two main types of COPD are chronic bronchitis[2] and emphysema,[3] and the most common symptoms of COPD are frequent coughing (a "productive" cough in which thick sputum/mucus is coughed up from the lungs), tightness in the chest and difficulty breathing after mild physical activities, and frequent lung infections such as pneumonia. Weight loss and depression are also common. In the advanced stages, due to shortness of breath, people reduce their physical activities, the skin of their fingers and toes may turn bluish, they may become confused, and they may experience frequent exacerbations and take longer

慢性気管支炎

肺気腫

湿（性）咳／喀痰

粘液

悪化

to recover from them. They often feel as if they are perpetually drowning.

(Reproduced [with modifications] with permission from Handbook of Disabilities by RCEP at the University of Missouri.)

Notes

❶ **chronic obstructive pulmonary disease（COPD）慢性閉塞性肺疾患**：chronic airflow obstruction（CAO）ともいう。病名や身体の構造，機能の英語は，たとえばParkinson's disease（人名にちなむ病名）や，Ebola fever（エボラ出血熱；Ebola＝アフリカ，コンゴ民主共和国北部の川。地名にちなむ病名）など，固有名詞にちなむもの以外は，通常，小文字で表記する。しかし，略語はそれぞれの頭文字をとって通常，COPDのように大文字で表記する。
略語は巻末に付しているが，学習者はまず，フルスペルを覚え，不用意に略語を頻用しないことが大切である。

❷ **bronchitis 気管支炎**：連結形bronch-(bronchus「気管支」)＋接尾辞-itis（炎症）

❸ **emphysema 気腫**：接頭辞en-(in「中」)＋physema（膨張)。文脈から明確でないときはpulmonary emphysema（肺気腫），mediastinal emphysema（縦隔気腫）のように部位を明記する。

☆ これだけは覚えておきたい英語

- **bronchitis** 気管支炎
- **contagious** 接触感染性の
- **emphysema** 気腫
- **mucus** 粘液
- **sputum** 喀痰

ことばのルーツ

• pulmon(o)- と pneumon(o)-, spir(o)- と -pnea

COPDのPはpulmonaryの略語である。この連結語pulmon(o)-は肺を意味するラテン語pulmoを語源とするが，ギリシャ語根pneumon(o)-も肺を意味する。例えば肺炎のことをpneumoniaという。肺は呼吸を司るvital organ（生命維持器官）であるが，呼吸を意味する連結形にはギリシャ語の-pnea（例；apnea「無呼吸」）とラテン語源のspir(o)-（例；respiration「呼吸」）がある。ちなみに，ラテン語のspiritusはもとはlife，soulの意味である。当時の人たちは，人が呼吸をしなくなること（死）は，魂が身体から出ていってしまうというイメージをもっていたのだろうか？

One-point Lesson

COPDの主な症状　Main symptoms of COPD

■ respiratory problems　呼吸障害

- difficulty breathing　呼吸困難
- frequent coughing　頻繁に咳をする
- sensitivity to cold and heat　寒冷，暑さに過敏
- sensitivity to highly polluted air　大気汚染の発生に過敏
- vulnerability to lung infections　肺感染症に冒されやすい

■ motor problems　運動障害

- difficulty climbing stairs　階段昇り困難
- difficulty carrying heavy objects　重い物を運ぶことが困難
- difficulty bending over　身体の屈曲困難
- difficulty walking long distances　長距離の歩行困難
- difficulty working in areas with high levels of dust or strong fumes
  ほこりの多い，あるいは強い煙霧のある場所での労働困難

Therapeutic Exercises for COPD (emphysema)
慢性閉塞性肺疾患（肺気腫）の運動療法

（イラストは柳澤　健（編）：イラスト理学療法ブラウン・ノート．メジカルビュー社，2007より引用）

リラクゼーション

Relaxation in a comfortable position

呼吸補助筋に対しファウラー位でのリラクゼーションを図る。

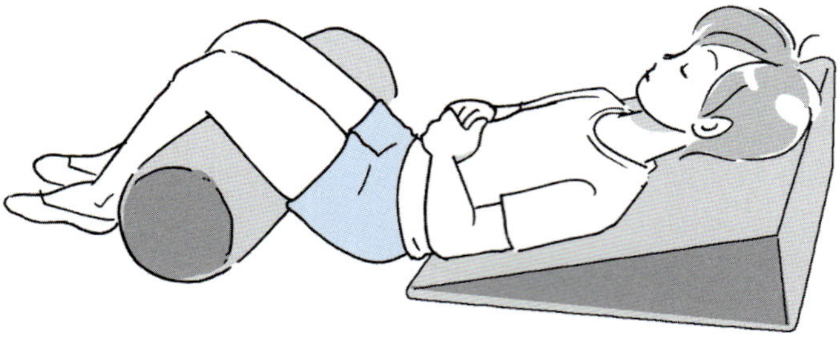

Instructions to the patient

Lie down on the cushions and relax. This will help to relax your accessory respiratory muscles.

クッションの上に横になって楽にしてください。これは呼吸補助筋をリラックスさせます。

腹式（横隔膜）呼吸

Diaphragmatic breathing

腹式（横隔膜）呼吸は吸気に合わせてお腹を膨らませるようにする。息を鼻からゆっくり吸い，口からゆっくり吐く。

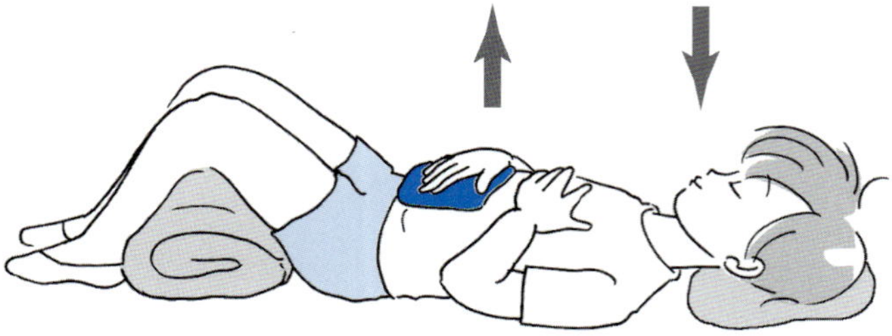

Instructions to the patient

I'd like you to get onto the bed and lie on your back. Just relax and breathe in slowly through your nose so that your stomach expands. Now breathe out slowly through your mouth.

ベッドに仰向けに寝てください。リラックスして，ゆっくり鼻から息を吸い込み，お腹を膨らませてください。次に，口をすぼませながらゆっくり息を吐いてください。

胸郭の柔軟性の維持（体幹の前屈）

Maintaining thoracic cage flexibility (trunk flexion)

胸郭の柔軟性を維持するため，呼気に合わせてゆっくり体前屈する。吸気に合わせてゆっくりと体を起こす。

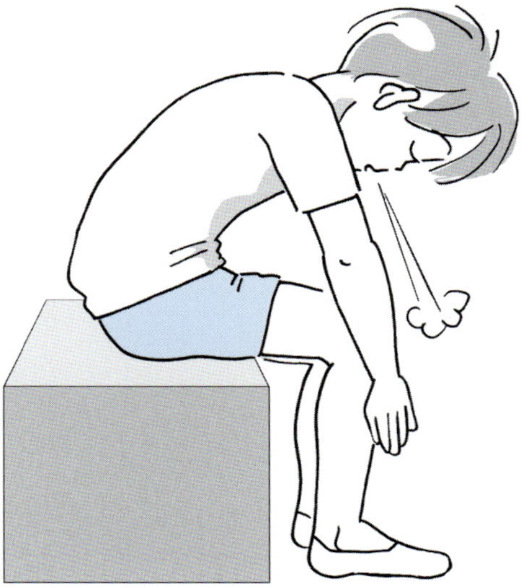

Instructions to the patient

Sit down on the stool and curl your body down as you breathe out. Now bring your body back up as you breathe in. This will help make your thorax more flexible.

イスに座ってください。息を吐きながら体を丸くして倒します。次に，息を吸いながら体を起こしてください。この運動は胸部の柔軟性を維持するのに効果があります。

座位でのパニックコントロール

Panic control in a sitting position

座位でのパニックコントロール（息切れが強くなり，パニック状態に陥ったときに楽な姿勢で呼吸を整える）は，上肢で体幹を支持するような前傾姿勢をとる。

Instructions to the patient

Just sit down facing the back of the chair. Now hold the back of the chair with both hands, lean forward, and breathe slowly.

椅子に逆向きに座って背もたれをもってください。体を前に曲げて，ゆっくり息をしてください。

INTRODUCTION
CHAPTER I
CHAPTER II
CHAPTER III
CHAPTER IV
APPENDIX

EXERCISES

1. COPDの完全な英語を書きなさい。

C ____________ O ____________ P ____________ D ____________

2. (1)～(5)の英語の説明に該当するものをa～eから選びなさい。

(1) bronchitis ( )
(2) exhale ( )
(3) pneumonia ( )
(4) pulmonary ( )
(5) sputum ( )

a. Inflammation of the mucous membranes of the bronchus
b. Lung inflammation caused by an infection
c. Mucus from the lungs
d. Relating to the lungs
e. To breathe out

3. 内容が正しい文にはTを，間違っている文にはFを記入しなさい。

(1)_____ COPD is a progressive and contagious disease.
(2)_____ The most common cause of COPD is smoking cigarettes.
(3)_____ Genetic factors are not related to COPD.
(4)_____ Among the most common symptoms of COPD are weight gain and chest pain.
(5)_____ COPD does not include psychological symptoms.

Dysphagia 嚥下障害

脳，脊髄，神経系の障害の１つであり，食物をスムーズに飲み込みにくい，あるいは，むせたり，のどにつまる症状をいう。パーキンソン病や多発性硬化症の症状にみられる。先天性の障害，咽喉部の外傷，頸部癌の存在なども考えられる。また，加齢につれて，食物を飲み込むことに必要な筋肉が弱まり，嚥下困難を訴える高齢者も多い。食べ物がのどにつまったり，誤嚥して気管に入り，肺炎を引き起こすこともあり，生命の危険にさらされることもあるので，注意を要する。

さらに，身体的要因ばかりでなく，恐食症（phagophobia）のような心理的要因による障害も知られている。

BACKGROUND INFORMATION

Dysphagia[1] is distinct from other similar symptoms like odynophagia,[2] which is defined as painful swallowing, and globus sensation, which is the sensation of a lump in the throat. Psychogenic dysphagia is known as phagophobia.[3]

odynophagia：嚥下痛
globus sensation：〔候の〕異和感
Psychogenic dysphagia / phagophobia：心因性嚥下障害／恐食症

Swallowing disorders resulting from congenital abnormalities, structural damage, and/or medical conditions can occur in all age groups. Swallowing problems are a common complaint among older individuals, and the incidence of dysphagia is higher in the elderly, in patients who have had strokes, and in patients who are admitted to acute care hospitals or chronic care facilities. Other causes of dysphagia include head and neck cancer, and progressive neurologic diseases such as Parkinson's disease, multiple sclerosis, and amyotrophic lateral sclerosis.[4] Dysphagia is a symptom of many different diseases, and the causative disease in individual patients can usually be determined through careful history taking by the treating physician and a formal dysphagia evaluation performed by a speech-language pathologist. Some patients with swallowing disorders do not have dysphagia, so the absence of this symptom does not exclude an underlying disease. Like breathing, which is normally accomplished without any forethought, swallowing can become awkward merely through focusing too intently on the process.

congenital：先天性の
complaint：病訴
amyotrophic lateral sclerosis：筋萎縮性側索硬化［症］

Dysphagia is classified into two major types: oropharyngeal[5]

oropharyngeal：口腔咽頭嚥下障害

dysphagia and esophageal dysphagia. In some patients with dysphagia, no organic cause can be found, and these patients are defined as having functional dysphagia.

食道嚥下障害

(Reproduced [with modifications] with permission from Handbook of Disabilities by RCEP at the University of Missouri. <http://www.rcep7.org/framefretxt.html>)

嚥下のプロセス

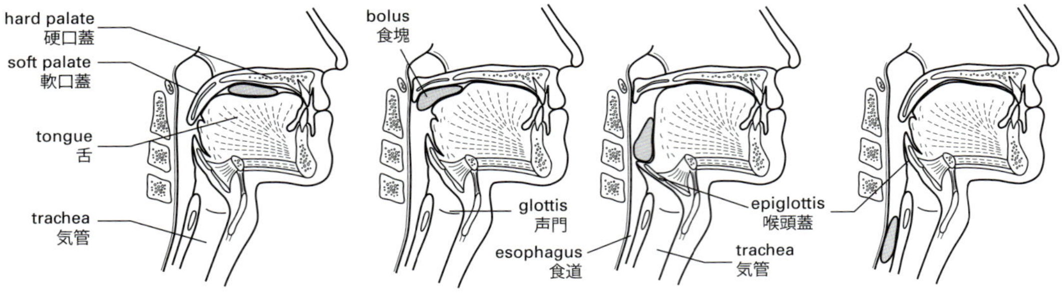

（A）　（B）　（C）　（D）

（A）食塊は舌が口蓋を押すことによって，口腔の後方に送られる。
（B）鼻咽頭が閉鎖する。
（C）咽頭括約筋が連続して収縮し，食塊を食道へと押し込む。気管が声門によって閉鎖され，喉頭蓋が声門上で閉じる。
（D）食塊は蠕動収縮によって食道を下降する。

Notes

❶**dysphagia　嚥下障害**：dys-（接頭辞「困難，不全」）＋phag-（連結形「食べる」）＋-ia（接尾辞「病的状態」）。発音[disféidʒiə]。dysphasia（失語症）と似た発音なので，混同しないこと。
❷**odynophagia　嚥下痛**：odyno-は「痛み」に関する連結形。
❸**phagophobia　恐食症**：-phobiaは「恐怖症」の意味。aquaphobia（水恐怖症），school phobia（学校恐怖症），anthropophobia（対人恐怖症）など。拒食症はanorexia。反意語は-philia（～への病的愛好）。
❹**amyotrophic lateral sclerosis　筋萎縮〔性〕側索硬化〔症〕**：a-（接頭辞「無，不」）＋myo-（連結形「筋肉」）＋trophic（連結形「～な栄養に関する」）。
❺**oropharyngeal　口腔咽頭の**：or(o)-（連結形「口」）＋pharyng-（連結形「咽頭」）＋（接尾辞-al「～に関する」）

☆ これだけは覚えておきたい英語

- **complaint**　病訴
- **congenital**　先天性の
- **dysphagia**　嚥下障害
- **esophageal**　食道の
- **odynophagia**　嚥下痛

ことばのルーツ

phag-　食べること

dysphagia, odynophagiaの連結形phag(o)-は，ギリシャ語でphagō（食べること）に由来する。phagomaniaとは貪食症。逆にphagophobiaは恐食症。食べるのは口からだけではない。身体の内部ではphagocyte（食細胞）が細菌や異物を食べて，phagocytose（食菌作用）をしてくれる。人は体の外からも内からも「食する」存在であるようだ。

EXERCISES

1. 文字の順を変えて，正確な英語に直しなさい。

(1) eal / oro / pharyng　(　　　　　　　　)

(2) genit / con / al　(　　　　　　　　)

(3) ia / dys / phag　(　　　　　　　　)

(4) normal / ab / ity　(　　　　　　　　)

(5) troph / a / ic / myo　(　　　　　　　　)

2. (1)～(5)の用語の説明に該当するものをa～eから選びなさい。

(1) complaint　(　　)

(2) congenital　(　　)

(3) dysphagia　(　　)

(4) odynophagia　(　　)

(5) sclerosis　(　　)

a. a condition in which soft tissue in the body becomes abnormally hard

b. a condition in which the patient experiences pain when swallowing food

c. difficulty swallowing as a symptom of disease

d. referring to a disease or medical condition that exists at or before birth

e. a symptom or medical problem that a patients says he/she has

Speech and Language Disorders　言語障害

言語障害には，言語の音声と発声が困難ではあるが言語を理解している「発声機能の障害」と，言語の理解と表現が困難な状態である「言語機能の障害」がある。

発声機能の障害には「音声(発声)障害」「構音障害」「吃音症」「痙攣性発声障害」「速話症」「乱雑言語症」「早口言語」などがある。言語機能の障害には「失語症」「高次脳機能障害」「言語発達障害」「知的障害」「自閉症」などがある。これらの障害は，先天性から，病気や外傷による後天性まで，小児から高齢者まで広範囲である。これら障害をもつ人の症状に合わせた訓練，指導，助言，援助は，主として言語聴覚士(ST)が他の専門職と協力して行う。病院では，リハビリテーション科，耳鼻咽喉科，脳神経外科のスタッフ，看護師とも連携をしながら，また，教育者，家族とも協力し合って，患者の言語訓練を行う。

BACKGROUND INFORMATION

Communication involves expressive language (speaking and writing), receptive language (listening and reading), and non-verbal communication (facial expressions and gestures). Speech and language disorders are medical conditions in which patients experience varying degrees of difficulty in communicating with others. They can occur in children or adults of any age.

表出性言語
受容性言語
身ぶり

Speech disorders　発声(音声)障害

Speech disorders involve impediments to producing sounds correctly or fluently, and include problems with the quality of voice (phonological processes). Many people with speech disorders cannot pronounce words correctly but have no problem understanding or reasoning. However, the differences between normal speech and disordered speech are not entirely clear.

音韻的過程

Speech disorders often involve dysarthria (an articulation disorder), which can be caused by strokes, Parkinson's disease, amyotrophic lateral sclerosis, surgical accidents, or cerebral palsy. Dysarthria can be:

- organic (a cleft palate or abnormally shaped lips cause pronunciation difficulties)
- dyskinetic (abnormal voluntary movement resulting from stroke or cerebellar incoordination)
- functional (morphological abnormalities of the articulation

構音障害
筋萎縮性側索硬化症(ALS)
器質性／口蓋裂
運動異常性
機能性／形態学的異常

organs lead to speech developmental delay)

- auditory (a secondary disorder caused by auditory abnormalities)
- stuttering (interruption of the flow or rhythm of speech)
- cluttering (abnormal or irregular speech delivery rate, similar to stuttering; can involve gibberish and aphasia)
- convulsive dysphonia (focal dystonia)
- apraxia (results from stroke or progressive illness and involves inconsistent production of speech sounds and the rearranging of sounds in a word)

Dysphonia

Dysphonia is difficulty in speaking due to a physical condition of the mouth, tongue, throat, or vocal cords. When people with dysphonia speak, the voice is hoarse, and the voice pitch and quality change.

発声障害

声帯

声の高さ

Language disorders 言語障害

Language disorders are dysfunctions in both expressive language (sharing thoughts and feelings) and receptive language (understanding other people). These disorders are due to brain disease (cerebrovascular disease). For example, stroke or cerebral infarction damages particular areas of the brain, which may result in the loss of hearing, speaking, reading, and writing abilities, or in medical conditions that make communications difficult. Language disorders are subdivided as follows:

脳梗塞

Higher-order brain dysfunction

This condition typically results from cerebral hemorrhage or thrombosis, cerebral infarction, or Alzheimer's disease. Patients have difficulty speaking and are unable to write.

Aphasia

Aphasia is the inability or impaired ability to speak or understand speech. It is caused by brain damage. When the Broca area in the frontal part of the brain is damaged, expressive

失語症

ブローカ野（中枢）

function (speaking or writing) is severely impaired; this is called expressive aphasia or motor aphasia. People with expressive aphasia may be able to speak fluently but without being able to communicate what they want to say. When Wernicke's area in the lateral part of the brain is damaged, the ability to understand spoken or written words is severely impaired; this is called receptive aphasia or sensory aphasia.

表出性失語〔症〕

受容性失語〔症〕

Language delay

言語発達遅滞

Language delay refers to a situation in which children fail to develop language skills at the expected age. Related disorders include the following:

- specific language impairment (SLI)

特異的言語発達障害

Children with SLI cannot or will not speak, and they show no interest in speaking in their preschool years. During its developmental stage, SLI is usually accompanied by learning delay. SLI is believed to be the result of a particular brain dysfunction, but its exact cause is unclear.

- autistic spectrum disorder(s)

自閉症スペクトラム障害

Evidence shows that language delay is commonly related to autism and attention deficit hyperactivity disorder (ADHD). However, Asperger syndrome, an autistic spectrum disorder, is not associated with language delay.

注意欠陥多動性障害

Language delay disorders are classified according to the brain area involved:

- developmental language disorder
- developmental aphasia
- dysgraphia
- developmental incoordination

言語発達障害，発達性言語遅滞

書字障害

発達性協調運動障害

Other causes of language disorders are:

- hearing loss
- intellectual delay
- mental disability

聴覚障害（聴覚喪失，難聴）

精神遅滞

- psychosocial deprivation
- developmental disability
- traumatic brain injury (TBI)

心理社会的剥奪
発達遅滞
外傷性脳障害

Treatment

Speech disorders and language disorders are distinct from each other. Therefore, the kind of treatment and rehabilitation should be determined carefully on the basis of examinations and evaluations. The treatment provided depends on the type of disorder, as well as the causes and symptoms. For example, disorders caused by physical deformities such as a cleft palate can be corrected by surgery.

身体的奇形

Speech and language therapists (STs) address problems with speech production, vocal production, swallowing difficulties, and language needs through speech therapy. For patients with aphasia, for example, STs use such aids as picture cards, videos, and audio recordings to help them recover their speaking, listening, reading, and writing skills.

…に取り組む

For patients who have had a stroke, muscular training of the lips, tongue, and throat should be started two weeks or so after the cerebrovascular accident to prevent a decline in muscular strength (disuse atrophy). In the convalescent stage, range of motion exercises of the hands and feet should be started to achieve recovery from paralytic dysarthria and to prevent articular muscle rigidity.

廃用性筋萎縮／回復期
麻痺性の

Rehabilitation for patients with speech and language disorders is provided by STs, PTs, OTs, medical doctors, dentists, psychiatrists, nurses, school nurses, teachers, and other specialists. The patients' family members also play an important role in the rehabilitation team. These specialists work together in various settings, including infant nursing facilities, special support classes at elementary schools, hospitals, rehabilitation facilities, and private practice.

児童養護施設
特別支援学級

☆ これだけは覚えておきたい英語

- **aphasia** 失語症
- **autism** 自閉症
- **autistic spectrum disorder** 自閉症スペクトラム障害
- **dysarthria** 構音障害
- **dysphonia** 発声障害
- **language disorder** 言語障害
- **stuttering** 吃音
- **speech disorder** 発声(音声)障害

One-point Lesson

脳卒中と言語障害

脳卒中によって言語中枢のある左大脳半球が損傷を受けた場合に，失語症が起きることがある。左大脳半球に言語中枢があると発見したのは，ドイツの神経科医Karl Wernicke(1848〜1905)とフランスの外科・神経科医，Pierre P. Broca(1824〜1880)である。それぞれの名前にちなんでウェルニッケ野(中枢) Wernicke's area(center)，ブローカ野(中枢) the Broca area(center)とよばれる脳の言語中枢のうち，前者は筋道のある会話と発話に必要な文を構成する役割を果たす。後者は，構音発生の指示を運動野(motor area)に送る。97%の人が左大脳半球に言語中枢を，残り3%は両半球にもっているといわれる。脳卒中が原因で言語機能が損なわれた場合，まず患者との信頼関係をつくっていきながら，その人の障害の程度，知識，興味のあることを考慮して，徐々に訓練を行っていくことが大切である。

EXERCISES

1. (1)〜(5)の英語の説明に該当するものをa〜gから選びなさい。

(1) aphasia ( )

(2) dysphonia ( )

(3) expressive aphasia ( )

(4) specific language impairment ( )

(5) stuttering ( )

a. difficulty in speaking because of physical condition of vocal organs

b. inability to speak and no interest in speaking in pre-school years

c. impairment of intelligence and adaptive behaviors

d. interruption of the flow or rhythm of speech

e. difficulty using language to share thoughts and feelings with others

f. loss of the ability to speak or understand speech caused by damage to the frontal or lateral part of the brain

g. motor aphasia caused by brain damage

2. 英語に相当する日本語をa〜iから選びなさい。

(1) cerebral hemorrhage ( )

(2) cerebrovascular accident ( )

(3) cerebral palsy ( )

(4) psychosocial deprivation ( )

(5) thrombosis ( )

a. 血栓症　b. 脳性小児麻痺　c. 脳血管障害　d. 脳出血

e. 外傷性脳損傷　f. 脳卒中　g. 梗塞　h. 精神遅滞　i. 心理社会的剥奪

3. 内容が正しい文にはTを，間違っている文にはFを記入しなさい。

(1)_____ Speech disorders may be defined as a defect in a person's ability to speak.

(2)_____ When Wernicke's area in the brain is damaged, people lose their ability to understand spoken or written words.

(3)_____ As speech disorders and language disorders have the same symptoms, rehabilitation for both is mostly entrusted to STs.

(4)_____ STs use aids like picture cards, videos, and audio recordings in the therapy they provide for patients with aphasia.

(5)_____ Muscular training of the lips, tongue, and throat should be started around two weeks after a patient has a cerebrovascular accident.

APPENDIX

Abbreviations
Index

Abbreviations リハビリテーション医療に関する略語

略語	原語	和訳
A		
AAE	active assistive exercise	自動介助運動
AAS	atlantoaxial subluxation	環軸〔関節〕亜脱臼
AB	asthmatic bronchitis	喘息性気管支炎
ABC	aneurysmal bone cyst	動脈瘤様骨囊症
ABD, Abd, abd	abduction	外転
ABI	ankle-brachial index	足首上腕比
	atherothrombotic brain infarction	アテローム血栓性脳梗塞〔症〕
ACh	acetylcholine	アセチルコリン《神経伝達物質》
ACL	anterior cruciate ligament	前十字靱帯
ADD, Add	adduction	内転
ADHD	attention deficit hyperactivity disorder	注意欠陥多動性障害
ADI	atlantodental interval	軸椎突起間距離
ADL, ADLT	activities of daily living [test]	日常生活動作〔テスト〕
AE	active exercise	自動運動
AEA, AE-amp	above elbow amputation	上腕（肘上）切断〔術〕
AED	automated external defibrillator	自動体外式除細動器
AFO	ankle foot orthosis [= SLB]	短下肢装具
AGN, agn	agnosia	失認〔症〕
AK	above knee	膝上
AKA	arthrokinematic approach	関節運動学的アプローチ
AKA, AK-amp	above-knee amputation	大腿（膝上）切断〔術〕
ALS	amyotrophic lateral sclerosis	筋萎縮性側索硬化症
AMC	arthrogryposis multiplex congenita	先天性多発性関節拘縮症
AMI	acute myocardial infarction	急性心筋梗塞〔症〕
AMP, amp	amputation	切断〔術〕
ANS	autonomic nervous system	自律神経系
APB	atrial premature beat	心房〔性〕期外収縮
APC	atrial premature contraction	心房〔性〕期外収縮
APDL	activities parallel to daily living	日常生活関連動作
APH	aphasia	失語〔症〕
ARE	active resistance exercise	自動抵抗運動
ARDS	acute respiratory distress syndrome	急性呼吸窮迫症候群
ARI	acute respiratory insufficiency	急性呼吸不全
AS	ankylosing spondylitis	強直性脊椎炎
	aortic stenosis	大動脈弁狭窄〔症〕
ASD	Alzheimer senile dementia	アルツハイマー型老年認知症
	atrial septal defect	心房中隔欠損〔症〕
ASO	arteriosclerosis obliterans	閉塞性動脈硬化〔症〕
AT	anaerobic threshold	無酸素性作業閾値
	Achilles tendon	アキレス腱
ATR	Achilles tendon reflex	アキレス腱反射

略語	原語	和訳
B		
BBT	basal body temperature	基礎体温
BE-AMP	below-elbow amputation	前腕切断〔術〕
BF	blood flow	血流
	body fat	体脂肪
	bone fragment	骨片
	biofeedback	バイオフィードバック
BI	Barthel index	バーセル指数
BKA, BK-amp	below-knee amputation	下腿切断〔術〕
BM	basal metabolism	基礎代謝
	body motion	体動
BMD	bone mineral density	骨塩密度
BMI	body mass index	体格指数《= 体重/身長^2 (kg/m^2)》
BMR	basal metabolic rate	基礎代謝率
	best motor response	最良運動反応
BP	blood pressure	血圧
BS	blood sugar	血糖
BT	behavior therapy	行動療法
BTR	biceps tendon reflex	上腕二頭筋腱反射
C		
CA	cardiac arrest	心停止
	cardiac arrhythmia	不整脈
CAB	coronary artery bypass	冠動脈バイパス〔術〕
CAD	congenital abduction deficiency	先天性外転欠損〔症〕
	coronary artery disease	冠動脈疾患
CAT	computer-assisted tomography, computerized axial tomography [= CT]	コンピュータ断層撮影〔法〕
CBR	complete bed rest	絶対床上安静
CCF	congenital clubfoot	先天性内反足
CCI	chronic coronary insufficiency	慢性冠状動脈不全〔症〕
CCM	congestive cardiomyopathy	うっ血性心筋症
CCU	coronary care unit	冠動脈疾患集中治療室
CDH	congenital dislocation of the hip	先天性股関節脱臼
CHD	congenital heart disease	先天性心疾患, 先天性心臓病
CI	cardiac index	心係数
	cardiac insufficiency	心不全
CM	cardiomyopathy	心筋症
CMJ	carpometacarpal joint	手根中手関節(CM関節)
CMO	cardiac minute output	毎分心拍出量
CMR, $CMRO_2$	cerebral metabolic rate of oxygen	脳酸素代謝率(消費量)
CNS	central nervous system	中枢神経系

略語	原語	和訳
CO	carbon monoxide	一酸化炭素
	cardiac output	心拍出量
COPD	chronic obstructive pulmonary disease	慢性閉塞性肺疾患
CP	clinical psychologist	臨床心理士
	cerebral palsy	脳性麻痺
CPM	continuous passive motion [device]	持続的他動運動〔装置〕
CRF	chronic renal failure	慢性腎不全
CSF	cerebrospinal fluid	脳脊髄液
CSFP	cerebrospinal fluid pressure	脳脊髄液圧
CSM	cervical spondylotic myelopathy	頸椎症性脊髄症
CSR	Cheyne-Stokes respiration	チェーン-ストークス呼吸
	continued stay review	継続入院検討
CT	cerebral thrombosis	脳血栓〔症〕
	cervical traction	頸椎牽引
	cognitive therapy	認知療法
	computed (computerized) tomography [= CAT]	コンピュータ断層撮影〔法〕
CTM	computed tomographic myelography	コンピュータ断層〔撮影〕脊髄造影〔法〕
CTS	carpal tunnel syndrome	手根管症候群
CVA	cerebrovascular accident	脳血管発作, 脳血管障害, 脳卒中
CVD	cardiovascular disease	心〔臓〕血管疾患
	cerebrovascular disease	脳血管障害, 脳卒中

D

DA	developmental age	発育年齢
DALE	disability-adjusted life expectancy	障害調整平均余命
DIA	death in action	運動死
DEFL	disease-free life expectancy	健康余命
DIP	distal interphalangeal	遠位指(趾)節間〔関節〕
DM	diabetes mellitus	〔真性〕糖尿病
DMARD	disease-modifying antirheumatic drug	寛解導入抗リウマチ薬
DNA	deoxyribonucleic acid	デオキシリボ核酸
DOA	date of admission	入院日
DVA	distance visual acuity	遠方視力

E

EBM	evidence-based medicine	科学的根拠に基づく医学(医療)
ECG	electrocardiogram [= EKG]	心電図
ECM	external cardiac massage	体外心臓マッサージ
ECR	extensor carpi radialis	橈側手根伸筋
ECU	extensor carpi ulnaris	尺側手根伸筋
EEG	electroencephalogram	脳電図
EKG	electrocardiogram [= ECG]	心電図
EMG	electromyography	筋電図検査〔法〕

略語	原語	和訳
EOA	examination, opinion, and advice	検査・評価・助言
EPA	eicosapentaenoic acid	エイコサペンタエン酸
ER	emergency room	救急室, 救急治療室, 救急外来
	external rotation	外旋
ERA	effective radiating area	有効照射面積
ERV	expiratory reserve volume	予備呼気量
ev	eversion	外反, 外がえし

F

略語	原語	和訳
FBS	fasting blood sugar [level]	空腹時血糖〔値〕
FCU	flexor carpi ulnaris	尺側手根屈筋
FDS	flexor digitorum superficialis	浅指屈筋
FES	functional electrical stimulation	機能的電気刺激
FFD	finger floor distance	指尖床間距離
FH	family history	家族歴
FIM	functional independence measure	機能的自立度評価法
FPL	flexor pollicis longus	長母指屈筋
FRC	functional residual capacity	機能的残気量
FRV	functional residual volume	機能的残気量
FSH	facioscapulohumeral [type]	顔面肩甲上腕型
FT	fatigue test	疲労検査
FVC	forced vital capacity	努力性肺活量
Fx	fracture	骨折

G

略語	原語	和訳
GA	general anesthesia	全身麻酔
GAD	general anxiety disorder	全般性不安障害
GAS	generalized arteriosclerosis	全身性動脈硬化〔症〕
GERD	gastroesophageal reflux disease	胃食道逆流〔症〕
GF	gastrofiberscope	胃ファイバースコープ
GOT	glutamic-oxaloacetic transaminase	グルタミン酸オキザロ酢酸トランスアミナーゼ
GPT	glutamic-pyruvic transaminase	グルタミン酸ピルビン酸トランスアミナーゼ

H

略語	原語	和訳
HB, Hb, HGB, Hgb	hemoglobin	ヘモグロビン
Hct	hematocrit	血沈値, ヘマトクリット
HNP	herniated nucleus pulposus	髄核ヘルニア, 脱出髄核
HR	heart rate	心拍数
HT, ht	heart	心臓
H&T	hospitalization and treatment	入院と治療
HT	heat treatment	温熱療法
	Hubbard tank	ハバードタンク

略語	原語	和訳
HTN	hypertension	高血圧〔症〕
	hypertensive nephropathy	高血圧性腎症
HTO	high tibial osteotomy	高位脛骨骨切り術
Hx, hx	history	病歴

I

IC	individual counseling	個人カウンセリング
	inspiratory capacity	最大吸気量
	intermittent claudication	間欠性跛行
ICD	International Classification of Diseases	国際疾病分類
ICIDH	International Classification of Impairments, Diseases, and Handicaps	国際障害分類
ICM	ischemic cardiomyopathy	虚血性心筋症
ICU	intensive care unit	集中治療部
IFN	interferon	インターフェロン
IL	independent living	自立生活
IM	intramuscular injection	筋肉内注射, 筋注
IMD	idiopathic myocardial disease	特発性心筋症
IP	interphalangeal	指節間の
	interstitial pneumonia	間質性肺炎
IPJ	interphalangeal joint	指節間関節
IPK	interphalangeal keratosis	指節間角化症
IQ	intelligence quotient	知能指数
IRDS	idiopathic respiratory distress syndrome	特発性呼吸不全症候群
IRV	inspiratory reserve volume	予備吸気量
IVH	intraventricular hemorrhage	脳室内出血
	intravenous hyperalimentation [= TPN]	経中心静脈栄養法

J

JRA	juvenile rheumatoid arthritis	若年性関節リウマチ

K

KAFO	knee-ankle-foot orthosis	長下肢装具
KB, K/B	knee brace; knee-bearing prosthesis	膝装具

L

LBP	low back pain	腰痛〔症〕, 下背部痛
LLB	long leg brace	長下肢装具
LCL	lateral collateral ligament	外側側副靱帯
LCP	Legg-Calvé-Perthes disease	レッグ－カルベ－ペルテス病
LD	lethal dose	致死量
LDH	lactate dehydrogenase	乳酸脱水素酵素

略 語	原 語	和 訳
LFT	left frontotransverse position	左前頭横位
	liver function test	肝機能検査
	low frequency therapy	低周波療法
LLB	long leg brace	長下肢装具
LLC	long leg cast	長下肢ギプス包帯
LLD	leg length discrepancy (difference)	脚長差
LOC	loss of consciousness	意識消失, 失神
LOM	limitation of movement	運動制限
LOS	length of stay	入院期間
LSCF	lumbar spinal canal stenosis	腰部脊柱〔管〕狭窄症
LUE	left upper extremity	左上肢
LV	left ventricle	左〔心〕室
LVDP	left ventricular diastolic pressure	左〔心〕室拡張期圧
LVH	left ventricular hypertrophy	左〔心〕室肥大

M

略 語	原 語	和 訳
MA	myofunctional appliance	筋機能矯正装置
MBC	maximal breathing capacity	最大換気量
MBP	mean blood pressure	平均血圧
MCI	myocardial infarction [= MI]	心筋梗塞〔症〕
MCL	medial collateral ligament	内側側副靱帯
	metaphyseal chondrodysplasia	骨幹端軟骨異形成症
MCR	metabolic clearance rate	代謝率
ME	medical engineering	医用工学
MED	medicine	医学, 医薬品
	multiple epiphyseal dysplasia	多発性骨端骨異形成症
MEFR	maximum expiratory flow rate	最大呼気流量比
METs	metabolic equivalent	運動強度の指標, 代謝当量
MFT	myofunctional therapy	筋機能療法
MG	myasthenia gravis	重症筋無力症
MI	maturation index	成熟度指数
	mental illness	精神疾患, 精神病
	myocardial infarction [= MCI]	心筋梗塞〔症〕
MIC	maximum inspiratory capacity	最大吸気量
ML	midline	中心線
MMS	mini-mental state examination	簡易知能テスト
MMT	manual muscle test	徒手筋力テスト
MP	metacarpophalangeal	中手指節の
MOB, mob, mobil	mobility	可動性, 移動性
MPJ	metacarpophalangeal joint	中手指節関節

略語	原語	和訳
MR	medical rehabilitation	医学的リハビリテーション
	mental retardation	精神遅滞
	metabolic rate	代謝率
MRA	malignant rheumatoid arthritis	悪性関節リウマチ
MRI	magnetic resonance imaging	磁気共鳴画像法
MS	mitral stenosis	僧帽弁狭窄症
	multiple sclerosis	多発〔性〕硬化〔症〕
	muscle strength	筋力
	morning stiffness	朝のこわばり
MSW	medical social work/worker	医療ソーシャルワーク, 医療ソーシャルワーカー
MTX	methotrexate	メトトレキサート
MW	microwave [therapy]	マイクロ波〔療法〕

N

略語	原語	和訳
NCVT	nerve conductivity test	神経伝導テスト
NR	nurse	看護師
NWB	non-weight bearing [brace]	免荷〔装具〕
NSG STA	nursing station	ナースステーション
NSAIDs	nonsteroidal anti-inflammatory drug	非ステロイド性抗炎症薬
NV, Nv	naked vision	裸眼視力

O

略語	原語	和訳
OA	osteoarthritis	変形性関節症
OALL	ossification of the anterior longitudinal ligament	前縦靱帯骨化症
OBS	organic brain syndrome	器質性脳症候群
OH	occupational history	職業歴
OI	osteogenesis imperfecta	骨形成不全症
ON	optic nerve	視神経
OPLL	ossification of the posteriorlongitudinal ligament	後縦靱帯骨化症
OR	operating room	手術室
ORT	orthoptist	視能訓練士
OT	occupational therapy/therapist	作業療法, 作業療法士
OYL	ossification of a yellow ligament	黄色靱帯骨化症

P

略語	原語	和訳
PCG	phonocardiogram; phonocardiography	心音図検査〔法〕
PCL	posterior cruciate ligament	後十字靱帯
PEF	peak expiratory flow rate	最大呼気流量
PEG	periodontology	歯周病学
PFI	physical fitness index	体力指数
PFT	pulmonary function test	肺機能検査
PHN	public health nurse	保健師
PIPJ	proximal interphalangeal joint	近位指節間関節

略語	原語	和訳
PKN	parkinsonism	パーキンソニズム
PLF	posterolateral lumbar fusion	後側方〔腰椎〕固定術
PMD	progressive muscular dystrophy	進行性筋ジストロフィ
PN	percutaneous nucleotomy	経皮的髄核摘出術
	pyelonephritis	腎盂腎炎
Pn	pneumococcus	肺炎球菌
PNF	proprioceptive neuromuscular facilitation	固有受容器性神経筋促通法
PNS	peripheral nervous system	末梢神経系
P&O	prosthetist and orthotist	義肢装具士
PRE	progressive resistance exercise	漸増抵抗運動
PSH	postspinal anesthesia headache	脊〔椎〕麻〔酔〕後頭痛
PSI	pulmonic stenoinsufficiency	肺動脈狭窄・閉鎖不全〔症〕
PSW	psychiatric social worker	精神保健福祉士
PT	physical therapy/therapist	理学療法，理学療法士
	paroxysmal tachycardia	発作性頻脈〔症〕
PTB	patellar tendon bearing socket prosthesis	PTB式（膝蓋腱荷重式）下腿義足
PTR	patellar tendon reflex	膝蓋腱反射
PT (E) S	prosthese tibiale (à emoitage) supracondylien socket	PT (E) S式ソケット
PV	pulmonary vein	肺静脈
PWB	partial weight bearing	部分荷重
PWC	physical working capacity	身体的作業能力
PWV	pulse wave velocity	脈波伝播速度

Q

QOL	quality of life	生活の質

R

R	roentgen	レントゲン《照射線量の単位》
RA	rheumatoid arthritis	関節リウマチ
	residual air	残気
	right atrium	右〔心〕房
RD	renal disease	腎疾患
RGO	reciprocating gait orthosis	交互歩行装具
Rehab	rehabilitation	リハビリテーション
REM	rapid eye movement	急速眼球運動，レム
REX	resistant exercise	抵抗運動
RF	rheumatoid factor	リウマチ因子
RICE	rest, ice, compression, and elevation	安静・冷却・圧迫・挙上《スポーツ傷害の応急処置》
ROD	renal osteodystrophy	腎性骨形成異常症
ROM	range of motion	関節可動域
ROM-T	range of motion test	関節可動域テスト
ROM-EX	range of motion exercise	関節可動域運動

略 語	原 語	和 訳
RSD	reflex sympathetic dystrophy	反射性交感神経性ジストロフィ《=ズデック〔骨〕萎縮 Sudeck's bone atrophy》
RV	residual volume	残気量
Rx	prescription	処方箋

S

SACH	solid ankle, cushion heel	固定足首とクッションヒール《サッチ足部》
SC	sciatic [nerve]	坐骨神経
	self-care	自己健康管理
	spinal cord	脊髄
SCI	spinal cord injury	脊髄損傷
	specific language impaired	特異的言語発達遅滞
SCS	spinal canal stenosis	脊柱管狭窄症
SD	strength-duration	強さ―時間
SEM	verbal sample evaluation method	言語標準評価法
SEP	sensory nerve-evoked potential	感覚（知覚）神経誘発電位
SF	synovial fluid	滑液
SHB	shoe horn brace	くつべら式短下肢装具
SHS	shoulder-hand syndrome	肩手症候群
SK	Swedish (Sweden) knee cage orthosis	スウェーデン式膝装具
SLB	short leg brace [= AFO]	短下肢装具
SLP	speech-language pathologist	言語病理学者
SLRT	straight leg raising test	下肢伸展挙上テスト
SLTA	standard language test of aphasia	標準失語症検査
SMD	spina malleolar distance	棘果間距離
SOMI	sternooccipital mandibular immobilizer brace	ソミーブレース
SPMA	spinal progressive muscular atrophy	脊髄性進行性筋萎縮〔症〕
SR	spontaneous respiration	自発呼吸
ST, SLP	speech and language therapist (speech-language pathologist)	言語聴覚士
SW	social work/worker	ソーシャルワーク，ソーシャルワーカー

T

TA	tibialis anterior [muscle]	前脛骨筋
TB	tuberculosis	結核〔症〕
TBV	total blood volume	全血液量
TCIA	transient cerebral ischemia attack [= TIA]	一過性脳虚血発作
TDI	thought disorder index	思考障害指数
TE	therapeutic exercise	運動療法
TEA	total elbow arthroplasty	人工肘関節全置換術
TENS	transcutaneous electric nerve stimulation	経皮的電気神経刺激〔法〕
TES	therapeutic electrical stimulation	治療的電気刺激〔法〕
THA	total hip arthroplasty	人工股関節全置換術
TIA	transient [cerebral] ischemic attack [= TCIA]	一過性脳虚血発作

略語	原語	和訳
TKA	total knee arthroplasty	人工膝関節全置換術
TLC	total lung capacity	全(総)肺気量
TMD	temporomandibular disease	顎関節症
	trochanter malleolus distance	転子果長
TMJ	temporomandibular joint	顎関節
TPN	total parenteral nutrition [= IVH]	経中心静脈栄養法，高カロリー輸液法
TPR	total peripheral resistance	全末梢抵抗
TRA	total replacement arthroplasty	全置換〔術〕
TSB	total spinal block	全脊髄麻酔
	total surface bearing trans-tibial (below knee) prosthesis	TSB式(全面荷重式)下腿義足
TT	tilt table	〔起立練習用〕傾斜台(起立台)
TUV	total urine volume	全尿
TV	tidal volume	1回換気量

U

略語	原語	和訳
UA	urinalysis	尿検査
UKA	unicompartmental knee arthroplasty	単顆人工膝関節置換術
US	ultrasound; ultrasonography	超音波検査〔法〕

V

略語	原語	和訳
VC	vital capacity	肺活量
VE	ventilation	換気
	visual examination	視力検査
	respiratory minute volume	分時換気量
	vitamin E	ビタミンE
VHD	valvular heart disease	心臓弁膜疾患
VL	vastus lateralis	外側広筋
	ventrolateral	腹〔側〕外側の
VR	vocational rehabilitation	職業的リハビリテーション
VR counselor	vocational rehabilitation counselor	職業復帰カウンセラー
VSD	ventricular septal defect	心室中隔欠損症

W

略語	原語	和訳
WAIS	Wechsler adult intelligence scale	ウェクスラー成人知能テスト
W/C, WC	wheelchair	車椅子
WHO	World Health Organization	世界保健機関
WLRT	well leg raising test	健側下肢伸展挙上テスト
WN	wave number	波数
WNL	within normal limits	正常範囲内

INDEX
英和索引

A

□ abduction 外転 ……… 25, 27, 29
□ abductor muscle of great toe 母趾外転筋 ……… 49
□ accidental ingestion 誤嚥 ……… 18
□ Achilles tendon アキレス腱 ……… 46, 84
□ —— rupture アキレス腱断裂 ……… 83, 92
□ Achilles tendonitis アキレス腱炎 ……… 92
□ aching 疼痛のある，うずく ……… 69
□ acromion 肩峰 ……… 33
□ active movement 自動運動 ……… 84
□ activities of daily living (ADL) 日常生活動作 ……… 18
□ acupuncture 鍼 ……… 69
□ acute 急性の ……… 68
□ adduction 内転 ……… 25, 27, 29
□ adipose cell 脂肪細胞 ……… 77
□ adjuvant analgesics 補助的鎮痛薬 … 69, 70
□ adrenal gland 副腎 ……… 56
□ akinesia 無動 ……… 99
□ alleviate 軽減させる ……… 13
□ alogia 会話不能 ……… 107
□ alveolus 肺胞 ……… 6
□ amphiarthrosis 半関節 ……… 42
□ amputation 切断 ……… 16
□ amyotrophic lateral sclerosis (ALS) 筋萎縮性側索硬化〔症〕 ……… 117, 118, 120
□ analgesic 鎮痛薬 ……… 71
□ anatomic structure 解剖学的構造 … 68, 69
□ aneurysm 動脈瘤 ……… 105, 106
□ angular motion 角運動 ……… 25
□ ankle joint 足関節 ……… 33
□ anterior 前方 ……… 22, 23
□ anterior cruciate ligament injury 前十字靱帯損傷 ……… 92
□ anterior dislocation 前方脱臼 ……… 85
□ anterior tibial muscle 前脛骨筋 46, 48, 49
□ anti-inflammatory drug 抗炎症薬 … 71, 86
□ aorta 大動脈 ……… 7
□ aphasia 失語症 ……… 106, 107, 121, 124
□ expressive —— 表出性失語〔症〕 ……… 122
□ motor —— 運動性失語症 ……… 107
□ receptive —— 受容性失語〔症〕 ……… 122
□ sensory —— 感覚性失語症 ……… 107
□ apraxia 失行症 ……… 107
□ arachnoid membrane くも膜 ……… 54
□ areolar tissue 疎性結合組織 ……… 77
□ armpit 腋窩 ……… 33
□ artery 動脈 ……… 6, 7
□ artery wall 動脈壁 ……… 105
□ arthritis 関節炎 ……… 75
□ rheumatoid —— (RA) 関節リウマチ ……… 75, 76, 78
□ arthrogryposis 関節拘縮 ……… 25
□ articular cartilage 関節軟骨 ……… 40, 42
□ articular cavity 関節腔 ……… 42
□ articular meniscus 関節半月 ……… 42
□ articulation 関節 ……… 42
□ ascending conduction route 上行性伝導路 ……… 54
□ aseptic necrosis 無菌壊死 ……… 65
□ assistive device 補助装具 ……… 77
□ atherosclerosis アテローム〔性動脈〕硬化症 ……… 104, 106
□ athlete 運動選手 ……… 4
□ atlas 環椎，第一頸椎 ……… 39
□ attention deficit hyperactivity disorder (ADHD) 注意欠陥多動性障害 ……… 122
□ audio-visual aid 視聴覚教材 ……… 19
□ autism 自閉症 ……… 19, 124
□ autistic spectrum disorder(s) 自閉症スペクトラム障害 ……… 122, 124
□ autoimmune disorder 自己免疫疾患 ……… 76
□ autonomic nervous system (ANS) 自律神経系 ……… 53, 56, 57
□ avulsion fracture 剥離骨折 ……… 63

□ axial skeleton 軸骨格 ……37
□ axilla 腋窩 ……33
□ axis 軸椎，第二頸椎 ……39
□ axon 軸索 ……52

B

□ ball and socket joint 球関節 ……43
□ bandage 包帯 ……88
□ biceps brachii 上腕二頭筋 ……46, 49
□ biceps femoris 大腿二頭筋 ……46
□ biceps muscle 二頭筋 ……48
□ biofeedback 生体自己制御 ……69
□ birth defect 出生時欠損 ……18
□ blood clot 血餅 ……105
□ bone 骨 ……6, 36, 40, 77
□ ——s of fingers 指骨 ……37
□ ——s of toes 指骨 ……37
□ calcaneus —— 踵骨 ……46, 83
□ cancellous —— 海綿質 ……40
□ carpal —— 手根骨 ……37, 38
□ facial —— 顔面骨 ……37
□ flat —— 扁平骨 ……40
□ hip —— 寛骨 ……37
□ hyoid —— 舌骨 ……37, 50
□ irregular —— 不規則骨 ……40
□ long —— 長骨 ……40
□ metacarpal —— 中手骨 ……37
□ metatarsal —— 中足骨 ……37
□ pneumatized —— 含気骨 ……40
□ short —— 短骨 ……40
□ tarsal —— 足根骨 ……37, 38
□ tongue —— 舌骨 ……37
□ upper arm —— 上腕骨 ……85
□ bone fracture 骨折 ……62, 64
□ bone marrow 骨髄 ……40
□ bone spurs 踵骨棘 ……92
□ brace 装具 ……16, 77, 88
□ brachial plexus 腕神経叢 ……55
□ bradykinesia 運動緩徐 ……99, 100
□ brain 脳 ……6, 54
□ brain case 脳頭蓋 ……37
□ break 切断 ……62
□ breathing 呼吸 ……8
□ bronchitis 気管支炎 ……112
□ bronchus 気管支 ……56, 57
□ bruising 打撲傷 ……85

C

□ calcaneal apophysitis 踵骨骨端炎 ……92
□ calcaneal tendon 踵骨腱 ……46, 49
□ calcaneus bone 踵骨 ……46, 83
□ calcium カルシウム ……36
□ callus 仮骨 ……62
□ cancellous bone 海綿質 ……40
□ capillary 毛細血管 ……6, 7
□ cardiac cell 心筋細胞 ……48
□ cardiac muscle 心筋 ……45, 48
□ cardiovascular system 心血管系 ……8
□ care giver; carer 介護福祉士 ……14
□ carpal bone 手根骨 ……37, 38
□ cartilage 軟骨 ……36, 40
□ articular —— 関節軟骨 ……40, 42
□ hyaline —— 硝子軟骨 ……77
□ caudal 尾側 ……22, 23
□ cecum 盲腸 ……7
□ celiac ganglion 腹腔神経節 ……56, 57
□ central nervous system (CNS) 中枢神経系 ……53, 54, 55, 57
□ cerebellum 小脳 ……52, 55, 57
□ cerebral artery 脳血管 ……56
□ cerebral infarction 脳梗塞 ……121
□ cerebrovascular accident (CVA) 脳血管障害 ……104
□ cerebrum 大脳 ……52, 55, 57
□ cervical plexus 頸神経叢 ……55
□ cervical vertebra 頸椎 ……55, 39
□ child welfare institution 児童福祉施設 ……18
□ chiropractic manipulation 指圧手技 69, 71
□ chondromalacia patellae 膝蓋軟骨軟化症 92
□ chronic 慢性の ……68
□ chronic bronchitis 慢性気管支炎 ……111
□ chronic low back pain 慢性腰痛 ……68
□ chronic obstructive pulmonary disease (COPD) 慢性閉塞性肺疾患 ……111, 112

□ ciliary ganglion 毛様体神経節 ……57
□ circulation 循環 ……53
□ circumduction 分回し ……29
□ clavicle 鎖骨 …… 33, 37, 38
□ cleft lip 口唇裂 ……18
□ cleft palate 口蓋裂 …… 18, 120
□ clinical psychologist (CP) 臨床心理士 …14
□ closed fracture 閉鎖骨折 …… 63, 64
□ closed reduction 非観血的整復術 …… 65, 86
□ coccygeal vertebrae 尾椎 ……39
□ coccyx 尾骨 …… 37, 38, 39
□ cognitive change 認知的変化 ……17
□ cognitive difficulty 認知障害 …… 104
□ cold pack 冷湿布 …… 16, 69
□ collarbone 鎖骨 …… 33, 37
□ colon 結腸 …… 7, 56
□ comminuted fracture 粉砕骨折 ……63
□ common fibular (peroneal) nerve
総腓骨神経 ……55
□ compact substance; compact bone
緻密質 ……40
□ complaint 病訴 …… 117, 118
□ complete fracture 完全骨折 ……64
□ compound fracture 複雑骨折 …… 63, 64
□ compression 圧迫 …… 84, 88
□ compression fracture 圧迫骨折 ……64
□ concussion 脳しんとう ……92
□ condylar joint 楕円関節 ……43
□ cone-shaped 円錐形の …… 6
□ congenital 先天性の …… 117, 118
□ connective tissue 結合組織 45, 75, 77, 78
□ conservative treatment 保存療法 … 77, 83
□ contagious 接触感染性の …… 111, 112
□ contract 収縮する ……45
□ contracture 拘縮 …… 76, 78
□ convalescent stage 回復期 …… 123
□ cooling down 整理運動，クールダウン …… 8
□ coronal plane 冠状面 ……23
□ crack 亀裂 ……62
□ cranial 頭側 …… 22, 23
□ cranial nerve 脳神経 ……54
□ cranium 頭蓋 …… 37, 38, 55
□ cross-legged sitting position あぐら位 32
□ crutch 松葉杖 ……16

D

□ day-care center 介護老人福祉施設 ……18
□ decubitus position 臥位 ……31
□ deformity 変形 ……62
□ deltoid muscle 三角筋 …… 46, 48, 50
□ dementia 認知症 ……19
□ dendrite 樹状突起 ……52
□ dense tissue 稠密な組織 ……36
□ depressed fracture 陥没骨折 ……63
□ depression 下制 …… 25, 26
□ depression 陥凹 ……83
□ depression うつ …… 107
□ descending conduction route
下行性伝導路 ……54
□ developmental disability 発達遅滞 … 123
□ developmental incoordination
発達性協調運動障害 …… 122
□ developmental language disorder
言語発達障害，発達性言語遅滞 …… 122
□ diabetes 糖尿病 …… 106
□ diaphysis 骨幹 ……40
□ diarthrosis 可動結合 ……42
□ difficulty breathing 呼吸困難 …… 113
□ digastric muscle 顎二腹筋 ……50
□ digestion 消化 ……53
□ disability 障害 …… 2, 4, 17
□ discoloration 変色 ……62
□ dislocated shoulder 肩関節脱臼 ……92
□ dislocation 脱臼 …… 85, 88
□ distal 遠位 …… 22, 23
□ distal radius fracture 橈骨遠位端骨折 …64
□ disuse atrophy 廃用性筋萎縮 …… 123
□ dopamine (DM) ドパミン…… 99, 100
□ dorsal 背側 …… 22, 23
□ dorsal flexion 背屈 …… 25, 27
□ dorsiflexion 背屈 ……28
□ dorsum of hand 手背部 ……33
□ dose 投与量 …… 100
□ duodenum 十二指腸 …… 7

□ dysarthria 構音〔構語〕障害 ……107, 120, 124
□ dysgraphia 書字障害 …………………… 122
□ dysphagia 嚥下障害 ……………117, 118, 118
□ dysphonia 発声障害 ………………… 121, 124

E

□ educational rehabilitation
教育的リハビリテーション……………………………14
□ elbow joint 肘関節 …………………… 33, 49
□ elevation 挙上 ………………… 25, 26, 84, 87
□ eliminate 除去する ……………………………13
□ ellipsoid joint 楕円関節 ……………………………43
□ embolic stroke 塞栓性〔脳〕卒中 ………… 105
□ embolus 塞栓……………………………… 105, 106
□ emergency treatment 応急処置 …………65
□ emphysema 〔肺〕気腫 ……………… 111, 112
□ employment security office 職業安定所 14
□ endocrine gland 内分泌腺 ……………………53
□ epidural injection 硬膜外注射 ……… 69, 70
□ epiphyseal injury 骨端線損傷 ……………64
□ epiphysis 骨端 ……………………………………40
□ esophageal 食道の ………………………… 118
□ esophageal dysphagia 食道嚥下障害 … 118
□ esophagus 食道 ……………………………………57
□ eversion 外返し ……………………… 25, 28
□ exacerbation 悪化 ………………………… 111
□ excretion 排泄 ……………………………………53
□ exercise regimen 運動法 ………………… 4
□ expressive aphasia 表出性失語〔症〕 … 122
□ expressive language 表出性言語……… 120
□ extension 伸展 ………………25, 26, 27, 29, 30
□ extensor retinaculum 伸筋支帯 …………46
□ external fixation 外固定 ……………………65
□ external rotation 外旋………………… 25, 29
□ external skeletal fixation 創外固定 ……65
□ extracapsular ligament 関節外靱帯 ……42

F

□ facial bone 顔面骨 ……………………………37
□ facial nerve 顔面神経……………………………56
□ fat embolism 脂肪塞栓症 ……………………65
□ fat pad 脂肪体 ……………………………………42
□ fatigue fracture 疲労骨折 ……………………64
□ fatty meat 脂肪に富む肉 ………………… 4
□ femoral neck fracture 大腿骨頸部骨折 …64
□ femoral nerve 大腿神経 ……………………55
□ femur 大腿骨 ………………………… 37, 38, 42
□ fibrous articular capsule 線維膜 ………42
□ fibrous cell 線維芽細胞 ……………………77
□ fibrous tissue 線維組織……………………85
□ fibula 腓骨 ……………………………… 37, 38
□ first aid 応急処置 ……………………………65
□ fissured fracture 亀裂骨折 …………………63
□ flat bone 扁平骨 ……………………………40
□ flexion 屈曲 ………………25, 26, 27, 29, 30
□ dorsal —— 背屈 ……………………… 25, 27
□ lateral —— 側屈 ……………………… 25, 30
□ palmar —— 掌屈 ……………………… 25, 27
□ plantar —— 〔足〕底屈……………… 25, 28, 87
□ flexor retinaculum 屈筋支帯 ………………49
□ floating rib 遊走肋骨 ………………………38
□ Fowler's position ファウラー位 ……………32
□ fracture 骨折……………………………… 16, 64
□ avulsion —— 剥離骨折 ……………………63
□ closed —— 閉鎖骨折 ………………… 63, 64
□ comminuted —— 粉砕骨折 …………………63
□ complete —— 完全骨折……………………64
□ compound —— 複雑骨折 …………… 63, 64
□ compression —— 圧迫骨折…………………64
□ depressed —— 陥没骨折 ……………………63
□ distal radius —— 橈骨遠位端骨折 ………64
□ fatigue —— 疲労骨折 ………………………64
□ femoral neck —— 大腿骨頸部骨折 ……64
□ fissured —— 亀裂骨折 ……………………63
□ green-stick —— 若木骨折 …………………64
□ incomplete —— 不完全骨折…………………64
□ linear —— 亀裂骨折…………………………63
□ oblique —— 斜骨折…………………………63
□ open —— 開放骨折 ………………… 63, 64
□ pathologic —— 病的骨折 …………… 62, 64
□ simple —— 単純骨折 ……………… 63, 64
□ spiral —— 螺旋骨折…………………………63
□ sprain —— 剥離骨折 ………………………63
□ transverse —— 横骨折………………………63

□ twisted —— 螺旋骨折 ……63
□ frontal plane 前額面 ……23
□ fusion 癒合 ……70

G

□ gastrocnemius muscle 腓腹筋……46, 49
□ genitalia 生殖器 ……56
□ gesture 身ぶり ……120
□ gland 腺 ……52
□ adrenal —— 副腎 ……56
□ endocrine —— 内分泌腺 ……53
□ lacrimal —— 涙腺 ……57
□ parotid —— 耳下腺……56, 57
□ sublingual —— 舌下腺 ……56, 57
□ submandibular —— 顎下腺 ……57
□ gliding joint 滑動関節 ……43
□ gluteus maximus muscle 大殿筋 ……46
□ gluteus medius muscle 中殿筋 ……46
□ golfer's elbow ゴルフ肘 ……92
□ greater trochanter 大転子……38
□ green-stick fracture 若木骨折 ……64
□ groin 鼠径部 ……33
□ groin pull 鼠径部損傷 ……92
□ groin strain 鼠径部捻挫……92
□ groin tear 鼠径部裂傷……92
□ gymnastics 体操 ……85

H

□ half side-lying position 半側臥位 ……31
□ hazard 危険 ……6
□ health professional 医療従事者……2
□ hearing impairment 聴覚障害，難聴 ……19
□ hearing loss 難聴，聴覚障害，聴覚喪失 19, 122
□ heart 心臓 ……6, 56, 57
□ heel 踵部 ……33
□ heel spurs 踵骨棘 ……92
□ hematuria 血尿 ……62
□ hemiparesis 片側不全麻痺 ……106
□ hemorrhage 出血 ……106
□ hemorrhagic 出血性 ……106
□ herbal remedy ハーブ療法 ……69
□ high blood pressure 高血圧 ……106
□ higher-order brain dysfunction
高次脳〔機能〕障害 ……17
□ hinge joint 蝶番関節 ……43
□ hip bone 寛骨 ……37
□ hip joint 股関節……33
□ home helper ホームヘルパー ……14
□ horizontal plane 水平面 ……22, 23
□ hot pack 温湿布 ……69
□ humerus 上腕骨 ……38, 49, 85
□ hyaline cartilage 硝子軟骨 ……77
□ hyoid bone 舌骨 ……37, 50
□ hypoglossal nerve 舌咽神経 ……56

I

□ ibuprofen イブプロフェン ……70
□ ice 冷却……84
□ ileum 回腸 ……7
□ ilium 腸骨 ……38
□ immobilizer 固定器具……88
□ immune system 免疫系 ……76, 78
□ impaired coordination 調和運動障害 … 100
□ impairment 障害……16, 17
□ impulse インパルス ……52
□ in-patient 入院患者〔の〕……13
□ incomplete fracture 不完全骨折 ……64
□ individual 個人……99
□ infant nursing facility 児童養護施設 … 123
□ inferior 下方 ……22, 23
□ inferior cervical ganglion 下頸神経節 …56
□ inferior dislocation 下方脱臼……85
□ inferior extensor retinaculum
下伸筋支帯 ……49
□ inferior mesenteric ganglion
下腸間膜神経節 ……56
□ inferior salivatory nucleus 下唾液核 …57
□ inferior vena cava 下大静脈 ……7
□ infirmity 虚弱 ……2
□ infraspinatus muscle 棘下筋 ……46, 48
□ injury 損傷，傷害，外傷 ……12
□ instep 足背部 ……33
□ intensity （症状の）強さ ……69
□ intercalated disc 介在板 ……48

□ intercostal nerve　肋間神経 ……………………55
□ intermediate　中間の ……………………23
□ internal fixation　内固定 ……………………65
□ internal organ　内臓 ……………………45
□ internal rotation　内旋 …………………25, 29
□ intervention　インターベンション，介入 12, 17
□ intervertebral disc　椎間板 …………… 39, 40
□ intervertebral foramen　椎間孔 ……………39
□ intestine　腸 ………………………… 6, 7, 45
□ intracapsular ligament　関節内靱帯 ……42
□ inversion　内返し ……………………25, 28
□ involuntary muscle　不随意筋 ……… 45, 47
□ irregular bone　不規則骨 ……………………40
□ ischemic stroke　虚血性脳卒中 ………… 106
□ ischial nerve　坐骨神経 ……………………55
□ ischium　坐骨 ……………………………38

J

□ jejunum　空腸 ……………………………… 7
□ joint　関節 ……………………………………42
□ ankle ——　足関節 …………………………33
□ ball and socket ——　球関節 ……………43
□ condylar ——　楕円関節 ……………………43
□ elbow ——　肘関節 …………………… 33, 49
□ ellipsoid ——　楕円関節 ……………………43
□ gliding ——　滑動関節 ……………………43
□ hinge ——　蝶番関節 ………………………43
□ hip ——　股関節 ……………………………33
□ knee ——　膝関節 …………………………33
□ pivot ——　車軸関節 ………………………43
□ plane ——　平面関節 ………………………43
□ saddle ——　鞍関節 ………………………43
□ shoulder ——　肩関節 ……………………33
□ synovial ——　可動結合 ……………………42
□ wrist ——　手関節 …………………………33
□ joint capsule　関節包 ……………… 40, 42, 86

K

□ kidney　腎臓 ………………………… 6, 56, 57
□ knee joint　膝関節 …………………………33
□ kneeling on the floor　正座 ………………32

L

□ lacrimal gland　涙腺 ………………………57
□ language ability　言語能力 ………………18
□ language delay　言語〔発達〕遅滞 … 18, 122
□ language disorder　言語障害 ……… 107, 124
□ large intestine　大腸 ………………… 7, 57
□ lateral　外側 ………………………… 22, 23
□ lateral abduction　外側外転 ………………27
□ lateral epicondylitis　外側上果炎 …………92
□ lateral flexion; lateral bending　側屈 ………………………………………… 25, 30
□ lateral head　外側頭 ………………………49
□ lateral malleolus　外果 ……………………33
□ lateral rotation　外旋 ………………………25
□ latissimus dorsi muscle　広背筋 …………46
□ learning disability　学習障害 ……………19
□ left rotation　左回旋 ………………………25
□ levator scapulae muscle　肩甲挙筋 ………50
□ ligament　靱帯 ……………………………… 6
□ extracapsular ——　関節外靱帯 …………42
□ intracapsular ——　関節内靱帯 …………42
□ patellar ——　膝蓋靱帯 ……………………49
□ linea alba　白線 ……………………………46
□ linear fracture　亀裂骨折 …………………63
□ little league elbow　リトルリーグ肘 ………92
□ liver　肝臓 …………………………… 56, 57
□ long bone　長骨 ……………………………40
□ long flexor of toes　長母指屈筋 …………49
□ long head　長頭 ……………………………49
□ long sitting position　長座位 ……………32
□ low back pain　腰痛 ………………………69
□ lower extremity; lower limb　下肢 ……37
□ lubrication　潤滑 …………………………75
□ lumbar plexus　腰神経叢 …………………55
□ lumbar vertebra　腰椎 ……………… 39, 55
□ lump　こぶ …………………………………76
□ lung　肺 ………………………………6, 45, 57

M

□ major pectoral muscle　大胸筋 …… 46, 50
□ malfunction　機能不全 ……………………99
□ manipulation　徒手整復 …………… 65, 86

INTRODUCTION CHAPTER I CHAPTER II CHAPTER III CHAPTER IV APPENDIX

□ [bone] marrow　骨髄 ……………………………40
□ masseter muscle　咬筋……………………………50
□ medial　内側…………………………………… 22, 23
□ medial abduction　内側外転 ………………27
□ medial epicondylitis　内側上果炎 …………92
□ medial head　内側頭 ……………………………49
□ medial malleolus　内果 ………………… 33, 49
□ medial rotation　内旋……………………………25
□ median nerve　正中神経 ………………………55
□ median plane　正中面 …………………… 22, 23
□ medical procedure　医学的処置 ………… 106
□ medical rehabilitation
医学的リハビリテーション…………………………14
□ medical social worker (MSW)
医療ソーシャルワーカー……………………………14
□ meditation　瞑想 …………………………………69
□ medullary cavity　骨髄腔…………………………40
□ membrane　膜 ………………………………………36
□ meniscus　半月板 …………………………………88
□ meniscus injury　半月板損傷 ……………………92
□ mental disability　精神遅滞 ……………… 122
□ mental disorder　精神障害 ……………… 107
□ mental health issue　精神衛生上の問題 …19
□ metabolism　代謝 ………………………………… 4
□ metacarpal bone　中手骨 ………………………37
□ metatarsal bone　中足骨 ………………………37
□ middle cervical ganglion　中頸神経節 …56
□ mineral　ミネラル …………………………………36
□ motor aphasia　運動性失語症 …………… 107
□ mucus　粘液……………………………… 111, 112
□ multiple sclerosis　多発〔性〕硬化〔症〕 ……19
□ muscle　筋肉 ……………………………6, 45, 50
□ abductor —— of great toe　母趾外転筋 49
□ anterior tibial ——　前脛骨筋 … 46, 48, 49
□ biceps ——　二頭筋 ………………………………48
□ cardiac ——　心筋………………………… 45, 48
□ deltoid ——　三角筋 ……………………… 46, 48, 50
□ digastric ——　顎二腹筋 …………………………50
□ gastrocnemius ——　腓腹筋 ………… 46, 49
□ gluteus maximus ——　大殿筋 ………………46
□ gluteus medius ——　中殿筋 …………………46
□ infraspinatus ——　棘下筋 …………… 46, 48
□ involuntary ——　不随意筋 ………… 45, 47
□ latissimus dorsi ——　広背筋 ………………46
□ levator scapulae ——　肩甲挙筋 ……………50
□ major pectoral ——　大胸筋 ………… 46, 50
□ masseter ——　咬筋……………………………50
□ mylohyoid ——　顎舌骨筋 ……………………50
□ occipitofrontalis ——　後頭前頭筋 … 46, 48
□ omohyoid ——　肩甲舌骨筋 …………………50
□ outer ——　表層筋 ………………………………46
□ rectus abdominis ——　腹直筋 ……………46
□ sartorius ——　縫工筋……………………………46
□ scalenus anterior ——　前斜角筋 …………50
□ scalenus medius ——　中斜角筋 …………50
□ scalenus posterior ——　後斜角筋 ………50
□ semimembranosus ——　半膜様筋 46, 48
□ skeletal ——　骨格筋 ……………………… 45, 47
□ smooth ——　平滑筋………………………… 45, 47
□ soleus ——　ヒラメ筋 …………………… 46, 48, 49
□ splenius capitis ——　頭板状筋 ……………50
□ sternocleidomastoid ——胸鎖乳突筋 48, 50
□ sternohyoid ——　胸骨舌骨筋 ……………50
□ striated ——　横紋筋 ……………………………47
□ stylohyoideus ——　茎突舌骨筋 …………50
□ teres major ——　大円筋 ………………………46
□ thyrohyoid ——　甲状舌骨筋 ………………50
□ trapezius ——　僧帽筋 ……………… 46, 48, 50
□ triceps brachii　上腕三頭筋 …………………49
□ triceps ——　三頭筋 ………………………………48
□ vastus medialis ——　内側広筋 ……………49
□ voluntary ——　随意筋 …………………… 45, 47
□ muscle belly　筋腹 …………………………………49
□ muscle fiber　筋線維 ……………………… 47, 48
□ muscle relaxant　筋弛緩薬 ……………………69
□ muscle weakness　筋力低下 …………………16
□ muscular system　筋肉系 ……………………45
□ musculus trapezius　僧帽筋 …………………46
□ mylohyoid muscle　顎舌骨筋 ………………50

N

□ narcotics　麻酔薬 ……………………………… 69, 71
□ nasal mucosa　鼻粘膜……………………………57
□ nature　性質…………………………………………19

□ nerve 神経 ……57
□ common fibular (peroneal) ——
総腓骨神経 ……55
□ cranial —— 脳神経 ……54
□ facial —— 顔面神経 ……56
□ femoral —— 大腿神経 ……55
□ hypoglossal —— 舌咽神経 ……56
□ intercostal —— 肋間神経 ……55
□ ischial —— 坐骨神経 ……55
□ median —— 正中神経……55
□ oculomotor —— 動眼神経 ……56
□ pelvic splanchnic —— 骨盤内臓神経 …57
□ radial —— 橈骨神経……55
□ spinal —— 脊髄神経 ……54
□ tibial —— 脛骨神経 ……55
□ ulnar —— 尺骨神経 ……55
□ vagus —— 迷走神経 ……56
□ nerve cell 神経細胞……52
□ nerve ending 神経終末…… 68, 69
□ nervous system 神経系 …… 52, 53
□ autonomic —— (ANS) 自律神経系
…… 53, 56, 57
□ central —— (CNS) 中枢神経系 53, 54, 55, 57
□ parasympathetic —— (PNS) 副交感神経系
…… 53, 57
□ peripheral —— (PNS) 末梢神経系
…… 53, 54, 55, 57
□ sympathetic —— (SNS) 交感神経系 …53
□ neurocranium 脳頭蓋 ……37
□ neuron ニューロン ……53
□ nodule 小結節 ……76
□ non-steroidal anti-inflammatory drugs
(NSAIDs) 非ステロイド性抗炎症薬 …… 69, 70
□ nucleus 核 …… 47, 48, 52
□ numbness 麻痺 ……85
□ nurse 看護師 ……14
□ nursing home 介護施設 ……16
□ nutrient 栄養素…… 4

O

□ oblique fracture 斜骨折 ……63
□ occipital part 後頭部……33
□ occipitofrontalis muscle 後頭前頭筋 46, 48
□ occupational therapist (OT) 作業療法士
…… 2, 13, 14, 17
□ occupational therapy 作業療法 ……17
□ oculomotor nerve 動眼神経 ……56
□ odynophagia 嚥下痛 …… 117, 118
□ omohyoid muscle 肩甲舌骨筋 ……50
□ open fracture 開放骨折…… 63, 64
□ open reduction and internal fixation
観血的整復固定術 ……65
□ opposition 対立 …… 25, 27
□ optimistic 楽観的……94
□ oral steroids 経口ステロイド類 ……69
□ oropharyngeal 口腔の …… 118
□ oropharyngeal dysphagia
口腔咽頭嚥下障害 …… 117
□ orthopedic 整形外科的 ……16
□ orthoptist (ORT) 視能訓練士 ……14
□ osteoarthritis (OA) 変形性関節症 75, 76, 78
□ osteoblast 骨芽細胞……36
□ osteomyelitis 骨髄炎 ……62
□ osteoporosis 骨粗鬆症 …… 62, 64
□ otic ganglion 耳神経節 ……57
□ out-patient 外来患者〔の〕 ……13
□ outer muscle 表層筋 ……46
□ outpatient clinic 〔外来〕診療所 ……18

P

□ pain 痛み，疼痛 ……68
□ palm 手掌 ……33
□ palmar flexion 掌屈 …… 25, 27
□ pancreas 膵臓 ……56
□ paralysis 〔完全〕麻痺 ……16, 95, 106
□ paraplegia 対麻痺 ……95
□ parasympathetic nervous system (PNS)
副交感神経系 …… 53, 57
□ parietal part 頭頂部 ……33
□ Parkinson's disease (PD) パーキンソン病 99
□ parkinsonism 振せん麻痺……99
□ parotid gland 耳下腺…… 56, 57
□ passive movement 他動運動……84
□ patella 膝蓋骨……37, 38, 42, 49, 88

□ patellar ligament　膝蓋靱帯……49
□ pathologic fracture　病的骨折　……62, 64
□ pelvic ganglion　骨盤神経節……56
□ pelvic splanchnic nerve　骨盤内臓神経…57
□ percutaneous　経皮的な……84
□ periosteum　骨膜……36, 40
□ peripheral blood vessel　末梢血管……56
□ peripheral nervous system (PNS)
末梢神経系……53, 54, 55, 57
□ personality change　人格変容……104
□ phagophobia　恐食症……117, 118
□ phonological process　音韻的過程……120
□ phosphorus　リン酸……36
□ physiatrist　リハビリテーション医……13, 14
□ physical deformity　身体的奇形……123
□ physical disability　身体障害……13
□ physical therapist (PT)　理学療法士
……2, 13, 14, 16
□ physical therapy　理学療法……16
□ physician　医師……68
□ pivot joint　車軸関節……43
□ plane　断面……23
□ plane joint　平面関節……43
□ plantar fasciitis　足底筋膜炎……92
□ plantar flexion　〔足〕底屈……25, 28, 87
□ pneumatized bone　含気骨……40
□ posterior　後方……22, 23
□ posterior cervix　後頸部……33
□ posterior dislocation　後方脱臼……85
□ postural instability　姿勢不安定……99
□ posture　姿勢……6
□ productive cough　湿性咳嗽……111
□ professional　専門家……2
□ progressive movement disorder
進行性運動障害……99
□ pronation　回内……25, 27
□ prone position　腹臥位，伏臥位……31
□ prosthetist and orthotist (P&O)
義肢装具士……14
□ proteinuria　たんぱく尿……62
□ protrusion; protraction　突出……25, 26
□ proximal　近位……22, 23
□ psychiatric social worker (PSW)
精神保健福祉士……14
□ psychogenic dysphagia　心因性嚥下障害 117
□ psychosocial deprivation　心理社会的剥奪 123
□ pubis　恥骨……38
□ public health nurse (PHN)　保健師……14
□ pupil　瞳孔……57

Q

□ quadriceps　大腿四頭筋……88
□ quadriplegia　四肢麻痺……95
□ quality of life　生活の質……16

R

□ radial nerve　橈骨神経……55
□ radius　橈骨……37, 38, 49
□ range of motion (ROM)　〔関節〕可動域
……25, 77
□ receptive aphasia　受容性失語〔症〕……122
□ receptive language　受容性言語……120
□ receptor　レセプタ，受容器……52
□ rectum　直腸……7
□ rectus abdominis muscle　腹直筋……46
□ recurrent dislocation　反復性脱臼……86
□ reduce　軽減する……86
□ reduced short-term memory
短期記憶減退……107
□ reflex arc　反射弓……52
□ rehabilitation　リハビリテーション，社会復帰 13
□ rehabilitation hospital
リハビリテーション専門病院……14
□ repair　修復……94, 95
□ reposition　復位，還納……27
□ reproduction　生殖……53
□ respiration　呼吸……53
□ rest　休息……84
□ retrusion, retraction　後退……25, 26
□ rheumatism　リウマチ……75
□ rheumatoid arthritis (RA)　関節リウマチ
……75, 76, 78
□ rheumatoid nodule　リウマチ小結節……76
□ rib　肋骨……37, 38

□ right rotation 右回旋 ··· 25
□ rigidity 固縮 ··· 99, 100
□ rotation 回旋 ··· 25, 30
□ routine work 日課 ··· 17
□ runner's knee ランナー膝 ··· 92
□ rupture 破裂 ··· 105

S

□ sacral plexus 仙骨神経叢 ··· 55
□ sacral vertebrae 仙椎 ··· 39
□ sacrum 仙骨 ··· 37, 38, 39, 42, 55
□ saddle joint 鞍関節 ··· 43
□ sagittal plane 矢状面 ··· 22, 23
□ sartorius muscle 縫工筋 ··· 46
□ scalenus anterior muscle 前斜角筋 ··· 50
□ scalenus medius muscle 中斜角筋 ··· 50
□ scalenus posterior muscle 後斜角筋 ··· 50
□ scapula 肩甲骨 ··· 33, 37, 38, 49
□ sedative 鎮静薬 ··· 71
□ self-help device 自助具 ··· 16
□ semi-sitting position 半座位 ··· 32
□ semilunar cartilage 関節半月 ··· 42
□ semimembranosus muscle 半膜様筋 46, 48
□ semiprone position 半腹臥位 ··· 31
□ sensory aphasia 感覚性失語症 ··· 107
□ serratus anterior muscle 前鋸筋 ··· 46, 48
□ Sever's disease シーバー病 ··· 92
□ severity 重症度 ··· 19, 94
□ shin splint シンスプリント, 脛骨過労性骨膜炎 92
□ short bone 短骨 ··· 40
□ shoulder blade 肩甲骨 ··· 33, 37
□ shoulder joint 肩関節 ··· 33
□ side-lying position 側臥位, 横臥位 ··· 31
□ simple fracture 単純骨折 ··· 63, 64
□ Sims' position シムス位 ··· 31
□ sitting position 座位 ··· 32
□ skeletal muscle 骨格筋 ··· 45, 47
□ skeletal system 骨格系 ··· 36
□ skeleton 骨格 ··· 36
□ skin 皮膚 ··· 6
□ skull 頭蓋 ··· 37, 38
□ sleep disorder 睡眠障害 ··· 107
□ sling 三角巾 ··· 88
□ small intestine 小腸 ··· 7, 56
□ smooth muscle 平滑筋 ··· 45, 47
□ smooth muscle cell 平滑筋細胞 ··· 47
□ social rehabilitation 社会的リハビリテーション ··· 14
□ social worker (SW) ソーシャルワーカー ··· 14
□ sole 足底部 ··· 33
□ soleus muscle ヒラメ筋 ··· 46, 48, 49
□ special support class 特別支援学級 ··· 123
□ specific language impairment (SLI) 特異的言語発達障害 ··· 122
□ speech and language therapist (ST) 言語聴覚士 ··· 2, 13, 14
□ speech disorder 発声障害, 音声障害 ··· 124
□ sphenopalatine ganglion 翼口蓋神経節 57
□ spinal canal 脊椎管 ··· 94, 95
□ spinal cord 脊髄 ··· 52, 53, 54, 55, 57
□ spinal cord injury 脊髄損傷 ··· 94
□ spinal nerve 脊髄神経 ··· 54
□ spine 脊柱 ··· 37, 38, 40
□ spinous process 棘突起 ··· 39
□ spiral fracture 螺旋骨折 ··· 63
□ splenius capitis muscle 頭板状筋 ··· 50
□ splint 副子, 副木, スプリント ··· 16, 77, 88
□ spongy substance 海綿質 ··· 40
□ spontaneous return 自発的回復 ··· 104
□ sports injury スポーツ傷害 ··· 83
□ sports medicine doctor; sports physician スポーツ医 ··· 14
□ sprain 捻挫 ··· 88
□ sprain fracture 剥離骨折 ··· 63
□ sprained ankle 足関節捻挫 ··· 86, 92
□ sputum 喀痰 ··· 111, 112
□ stammering 吃 ··· 19
□ standing position 立位 ··· 32
□ stational bicycle 〔訓練用〕固定式自転車 ··· 16
□ sternocleidomastoid muscle 胸鎖乳突筋 ··· 48, 50
□ sternohyoid muscle 胸骨舌骨筋 ··· 50
□ sternum 胸骨 ··· 37, 38
□ stiffness 硬直 ··· 75

□ stimulus; [pl] stimuli　刺激 ……6, 52, 53
□ stomach　胃 …… 6, 45, 56, 57
□ strain　挫傷 ……86
□ striated muscle　横紋筋 ……47
□ stripe　黄紋 …… 47, 48
□ stroke　脳卒中 …… 16, 19, 104, 106
□ 　embolic ——　塞栓性〔脳〕卒中 …… 105
□ 　ischemic ——　虚血性脳卒中 …… 106
□ 　thrombotic ——　血栓性〔脳〕卒中　105, 106
□ stumbling　つまずくこと ……85
□ stuttering　吃音 …… 124
□ stylohyoideus muscle　茎突舌骨筋 ……50
□ sublingual gland　舌下腺 …… 56, 57
□ submandibular ganglion　顎下神経節 …57
□ submandibular gland　顎下腺 ……57
□ substantia nigra　黒質 …… 99, 100
□ Sudeck's atrophy　ズーデック骨萎縮 ……65
□ superficial　表在の ……23
□ superficial cell　表層細胞 ……77
□ superior　上方 …… 22, 23
□ superior cervical ganglion　上頸神経節　56
□ superior extensor retinaculum
上伸筋支帯 ……49
□ superior mesenteric ganglion
上腸間膜神経節 ……56
□ superior salivatory nucleus　上唾液核 …57
□ superior vena cava　上大静脈 …… 7
□ supination　回外 …… 25, 27
□ supine position　仰臥位 ……31
□ swallowing　嚥下 ……18
□ swelling　腫れ ……62
□ symmetrical　対称的な ……76
□ sympathetic nervous system (SNS)
交感神経系 ……53
□ synapse　シナプス，接合部 ……52
□ synarthrosis　不動結合 ……42
□ synovial bursa　滑液包 ……42
□ synovial fluid　滑液 ……77
□ synovial joint　可動結合 ……42
□ synovial membrane　滑膜 …… 42, 77
□ synovium　滑膜 ……76

T

□ tarsal bone　足根骨 …… 37, 38
□ tenderness　圧痛 ……87
□ tendon　腱 ……6, 42, 45
□ tendon suture　腱縫合 ……84
□ tennis elbow　テニス肘 ……92
□ teres major muscle　大円筋 ……46
□ Terminologia Anatomica (TA)
解剖学用語 ……44
□ tetraplegia　四肢麻痺 ……95
□ thoracic cage　胸郭 ……37
□ thoracic vertebra　胸椎 …… 39, 55
□ thrombotic stroke　血栓性〔脳〕卒中
…… 105, 106
□ thrombus　血栓 …… 105, 106
□ thyrohyoid muscle　甲状舌骨筋 ……50
□ tibia　脛骨 …… 37, 38, 42, 49
□ tibial nerve　脛骨神経 ……55
□ tissue　組織 ……36
□ tongue bone　舌骨 ……37
□ torn rotator cuff　回旋筋腱板裂傷 ……92
□ traction　牽引 …… 65, 69, 71
□ transcutaneous electrical nerve
stimulation (TENS)　経皮的電気神経刺激
…… 69, 70
□ transverse fracture　横骨折 ……63
□ transverse plane　横断面 …… 22, 23
□ trapezius muscle　僧帽筋 …… 46, 48, 50
□ trauma　外傷 ……64
□ traumatic brain injury (TBI)
外傷性脳障害 …… 123
□ traumatic myositis ossificans
外傷性骨化性筋炎 ……65
□ tremor　振せん …… 99, 100
□ triceps brachii　上腕三頭筋 ……49
□ triceps muscle　三頭筋 ……48
□ twisted fracture　螺旋骨折 ……63

U

□ ulna　尺骨 …… 37, 38, 49
□ ulnar nerve　尺骨神経 ……55
□ ultrasound　超音波 ……69

□ ultraviolet light 紫外線 ······16
□ upper arm bone 上腕骨 ······85
□ upper extremity; upper limb 上肢 ······37
□ urinary bladder 膀胱 ······56, 57

V

□ vagus nerve 迷走神経 ······56
□ valgus 外反 ······25
□ varus 内反 ······25
□ vastus medialis muscle 内側広筋 ······49
□ vein 静脈 ······6, 7
□ ventral 腹側 ······22, 23
□ vertebra; [pl] vertebrae 椎骨 ··· 37, 39, 40
□ cervical —— 頸椎 ······55, 39
□ coccygeal —— 尾椎 ······39
□ lumbar —— 腰椎 ······39, 55
□ sacral —— 仙椎 ······39
□ thoracic —— 胸椎 ······39, 55
□ vertebral canal 脊椎管 ······95
□ vertebral column 脊柱 ······37, 38, 39, 40
□ vertebral disc 椎間板 ······40
□ viscerocranium 内臓頭蓋 ······37
□ vital organ 生命維持器官 ······6
□ vitamin deficiency disorder
ビタミン欠乏障害 ······62
□ vocal cord 声帯 ······121
□ vocational assessment 職業評価 ······14
□ vocational counseling 職業カウンセリング ······14
□ vocational rehabilitation
職業的リハビリテーション ······14
□ vocational rehabilitation (VR) counselor
職業復帰カウンセラー ······14
□ vocational training 職業訓練 ······14
□ Volkmann's contracture フォルクマン拘縮 ······65
□ voluntary muscle 随意筋 ······45, 47

W

□ walking stick 杖 ······77
□ warm-up 準備運動 ······8
□ well-being 健康で幸せな状態 ······2
□ wheelchair 車椅子 ······16
□ workplace 職場 ······14
□ World Health Organization (WHO)
世界保健機関 ······2,3
□ wrist joint 手関節 ······33

INDEX
和英索引

あ

□ アキレス腱　Achilles tendon ………… 46, 84
□ ——断裂　Achilles tendon rupture ………… 83, 92
□ アキレス腱炎　Achilles tendonitis ………… 92
□ あぐら位　cross-legged sitting position ………… 32
□ アセチルコリン　acetylcholine ………… 99
□ 悪化　exacerbation ………… 111
□ 圧痛　tenderness ………… 87
□ 圧迫　compression ………… 84, 88
□ 圧迫骨折　compression fracture ………… 64
□ アテローム〔性動脈〕硬化症　atherosclerosis 104, 106
□ 鞍関節　saddle joint ………… 43
□ 胃　stomach ………… 6, 45, 56, 57
□ 医学的処置　medical procedure ………… 106
□ 医学的リハビリテーション　medical rehabilitation 14
□ 医師　physician ………… 68
□ 痛み　pain ………… 68
□ イブプロフェン　ibuprofen ………… 70
□ 医療従事者　health professional ………… 2
□ 医療ソーシャルワーカー　medical social worker (MSW) ………… 14
□ インターベンション　intervention ………… 12
□ インパルス　impulse ………… 52
□ うずく　aching ………… 69
□ 内返し　inversion ………… 25, 28
□ うつ　depression ………… 107
□ 運動緩徐　bradykinesia ………… 99, 100
□ 運動性失語症　motor aphasia ………… 107
□ 運動選手　athlete ………… 4
□ 運動法　exercise regimen ………… 4
□ 栄養素　nutrient ………… 4
□ 腋窩　axilla; armpit ………… 33
□ 遠位　distal ………… 22, 23
□ 嚥下　swallowing ………… 18
□ 嚥下障害　dysphagia ………… 117, 118
□ 嚥下痛　odynophagia ………… 117, 118
□ 円錐形の　cone-shaped ………… 6
□ 横臥位　side-lying position ………… 31
□ 応急処置　emergency treatment; first aid ………… 65
□ 横断面　transverse plane ………… 22, 23
□ 黄紋　stripe ………… 47, 48
□ 横紋筋　striated muscle ………… 47
□ 音韻的過程　phonological process ………… 120
□ 温湿布　hot pack ………… 69
□ 音声障害　speech disorder ………… 124

か

□ 臥位　decubitus position ………… 31
□ 外果　lateral malleolus ………… 33
□ 回外　supination ………… 25, 27
□ 介護施設　nursing home ………… 16
□ 外固定　external fixation ………… 65
□ 介護福祉士　care giver; carer ………… 14
□ 介護老人福祉施設　day-care center ………… 18
□ 介在板　intercalated disc ………… 48
□ 外傷　injury; trauma ………… 12, 64
□ 外傷性骨化性筋炎　traumatic myositis ossificans 65
□ 外傷性脳障害　traumatic brain injury (TBI) … 123
□ 回旋　rotation ………… 25, 30
□ 外旋　external rotation; lateral rotation ………… 25, 29
□ 回旋筋腱板裂傷　torn rotator cuff ………… 92
□ 外側外転　lateral abduction ………… 27
□ 外側上果炎　lateral epicondylitis ………… 92
□ 外側頭　lateral head ………… 49
□ 外側の　lateral ………… 22, 23
□ 回腸　ileum ………… 7
□ 外転　abduction ………… 25, 27, 29
□ 回内　pronation ………… 25, 27
□ 介入　intervention ………… 17
□ 外反　valgus ………… 25
□ 回復期　convalescent stage ………… 123
□ 解剖学的構造　anatomic structure ………… 68, 69
□ 解剖学用語　Terminologia Anatomica (TA) ………… 44
□ 開放骨折　open fracture ………… 63, 64
□ 開放整復　open reduction ………… 86
□ 海綿質　spongy substance; cancellous bone ………… 40

□ 外来患者〔の〕 out-patient ……13
□ 外来診療所 outpatient clinic ……18
□ 会話不能 alogia ……107
□ 下頸神経節 inferior cervical ganglion ……56
□ 核 nucleus ……47, 48, 52
□ 角運動 angular motion ……25
□ 顎下神経節 submandibular ganglion ……57
□ 顎下腺 submandibular gland ……57
□ 学習障害 learning disability ……19
□ 顎舌骨筋 mylohyoid muscle ……50
□ 喀痰 sputum ……111, 112
□ 顎二腹筋 digastric muscle ……50
□ 下行性伝導路 descending conduction route ……54
□ 仮骨 callus ……62
□ 下肢 lower extremity; lower limb ……37
□ 下伸筋支帯 inferior extensor retinaculum ……49
□ 下制 depression ……25, 26
□ 下唾液核 inferior salivatory nucleus ……57
□ 下大静脈 inferior vena cava ……7
□ 肩関節 shoulder joint ……33
□ 肩関節脱臼 dislocated shoulder ……92
□ 下腸間膜神経節 inferior mesenteric ganglion ……56
□ 滑液 synovial fluid ……77
□ 滑液包 synovial bursa ……42
□ 滑動関節 gliding joint ……43
□ 滑膜 synovial membrane; synovium ……42, 76, 77
□ 可動域 range of motion ……77
□ 可動結合 diarthrosis; synovial joint ……42
□ 下方 inferior ……22, 23
□ 下方脱臼 inferior dislocation ……85
□ カルシウム calcium ……36
□ 陥凹 depression ……83
□ 感覚性失語症 sensory aphasia ……107
□ 含気骨 pneumatized bone ……40
□ 看護師 nurse ……14
□ 寛骨 hip bone ……37
□ 冠状面 coronal plane ……23
□ 関節 joint; articulation ……42
□ 肩―― shoulder joint ……33
□ 股―― hip joint ……33
□ 足―― ankle joint ……33
□ 手―― wrist joint ……33
□ 膝―― knee joint ……33
□ 肘―― elbow joint ……33, 49
□ 関節炎 arthritis ……75
□ 関節外靱帯 extracapsular ligament ……42
□ 関節可動域 range of motion (ROM) ……25
□ 関節腔 articular cavity ……42
□ 関節拘縮 arthrogryposis ……25
□ 関節内靱帯 intracapsular ligament ……42
□ 関節軟骨 articular cartilage ……40, 42
□ 関節半月 articular meniscus; semilunar cartilage 42
□ 関節包 joint capsule ……40, 42, 86
□ 関節リウマチ rheumatoid arthritis (RA) 75, 76, 78
□ 完全骨折 complete fracture ……64
□ 完全麻痺 paralysis ……106
□ 肝臓 liver ……56, 57
□ 環椎 atlas ……39
□ 還納 reposition ……27
□ 陥没骨折 depressed fracture ……63
□ 顔面骨 facial bone ……37
□ 顔面神経 facial nerve ……56
□ 気管支 bronchus ……56, 57
□ 気管支炎 bronchitis ……112
□ 危険 hazard ……6
□ 義肢装具士 prosthetist and orthotist (P&O) ……14
□ 吃 stammering ……19
□ 吃音 stuttering ……124
□ 機能不全 malfunction ……99
□ 球関節 ball and socket joint ……43
□ 休息 rest ……84
□ 教育的リハビリテーション educational rehabilitation ……14
□ 仰臥位 supine position ……31
□ 胸郭 thoracic cage ……37
□ 胸骨 sternum ……37, 38
□ 胸骨舌骨筋 sternohyoid muscle ……50
□ 胸鎖乳突筋 sternocleidomastoid muscle ……48, 50
□ 恐食症 phagophobia ……117, 118
□ 胸椎 thoracic vertebra ……39, 55
□ 棘下筋 infraspinatus muscle ……46, 48
□ 棘突起 spinous process ……39
□ 虚血性脳卒中 ischemic stroke ……106
□ 虚弱 infirmity ……2

INTRODUCTION
CHAPTER I
CHAPTER II
CHAPTER III
CHAPTER IV
APPENDIX

□ 挙上 elevation ······ 25, 26, 84, 87
□ 亀裂 crack ······ 62
□ 亀裂骨折 fissured fracture; linear fracture ······ 63
□ 近位 proximal ······ 22, 23
□ 筋萎縮性側索硬化〔症〕 amyotrophic lateral sclerosis (ALS) ······ 117, 118, 120
□ 筋弛緩薬 muscle relaxant ······ 69
□ 筋線維 muscle fiber ······ 47, 48
□ 筋肉 muscle ······ 6, 45, 50
□ 筋肉系 muscular system ······ 45
□ 筋腹 muscle belly ······ 49
□ 筋力低下 muscle weakness ······ 16
□ 空腸 jejunum ······ 7
□ 屈曲 flexion ······ 25, 26, 27, 29, 30
□ 屈筋支帯 flexor retinaculum ······ 49
□ くも膜 arachnoid membrane ······ 54
□ 車椅子 wheelchair ······ 16
□ 軽減させる alleviate ······ 13
□ 経口ステロイド類 oral steroids ······ 69
□ 脛骨 tibia ······ 37, 38, 42, 49
□ 脛骨神経 tibial nerve ······ 55
□ 脛骨過労性骨膜炎 shin splint ······ 92
□ 頸神経叢 cervical plexus ······ 55
□ 頸椎 cervical vertebra ······ 39, 55
□ 茎突舌骨筋 stylohyoideus muscle ······ 50
□ 経皮的電気神経刺激 transcutaneous electrical nerve stimulation (TENS) ······ 69, 70
□ 結合組織 connective tissue ······ 45, 75, 77, 78
□ 血栓 thrombus ······ 105, 106
□ 血栓性〔脳〕卒中 thrombotic stroke ······ 105, 106
□ 結腸 colon ······ 7, 56
□ 血尿 hematuria ······ 62
□ 血餅 blood clot ······ 105
□ 腱 tendon ······ 6, 42, 45
□ 牽引 traction ······ 65, 69, 71
□ 言語〔発達〕遅滞 language delay ······ 18
□ 肩甲骨 shoulder blade; scapula ······ 33, 37, 38
□ 肩甲挙筋 levator scapulae muscle ······ 50
□ 肩甲骨 scapula ······ 33, 49
□ 肩甲舌骨筋 omohyoid muscle ······ 50
□ 言語障害 language disorder ······ 107, 124
□ 言語聴覚士 speech and language therapist (ST) ······ 2, 13, 14
□ 言語能力 language ability ······ 18
□ 言語発達障害 developmental language disorder 122
□ 言語発達遅滞 language delay ······ 122
□ 肩峰 acromion ······ 33
□ 腱縫合 tendon suture ······ 84
□ 抗炎症薬 anti-inflammatory drug ······ 71, 86
□ 構音（構語）障害 dysarthria ······ 107, 120, 124
□ 口蓋裂 cleft palate ······ 18, 120
□ 交感神経系 sympathetic nervous system (SNS) ··· 53
□ 高次脳（機能）障害 higher-order brain dysfunction 17
□ 咬筋 masseter muscle ······ 50
□ 口腔咽頭嚥下障害 oropharyngeal dysphagia ··· 117
□ 口腔の oropharyngeal ······ 118
□ 後頸部 posterior cervix ······ 33
□ 高血圧 high blood pressure ······ 106
□ 後斜角筋 scalenus posterior muscle ······ 50
□ 拘縮 contracture ······ 76, 78
□ 甲状舌骨筋 thyrohyoid muscle ······ 50
□ 口唇裂 cleft lip ······ 18
□ 後退 retrusion; retraction ······ 25, 26
□ 硬直 stiffness ······ 75
□ 後頭前頭筋 occipitofrontalis muscle ······ 46, 48
□ 後頭部 occipital part ······ 33
□ 広背筋 latissimus dorsi muscle ······ 46
□ 後方 posterior ······ 22, 23
□ 後方脱臼 posterior dislocation ······ 85
□ 硬膜外注射 epidural injection ······ 69, 70
□ 誤嚥 accidental ingestion ······ 18
□ 股関節 hip joint ······ 33
□ 呼吸 breathing; respiration ······ 8, 53
□ 呼吸困難 difficulty breathing ······ 113
□ 黒質 substantia nigra ······ 99, 100
□ 固縮 rigidity ······ 99, 100
□ 個人 individual ······ 99
□ 骨格 skeleton ······ 36
□ 骨格筋 skeletal muscle ······ 45, 47
□ 骨格系 skeletal system ······ 36
□ 骨芽細胞 osteoblast ······ 36
□ 骨幹 diaphysis ······ 40
□ 骨髄 (bone) marrow ······ 40

□ 骨髄炎 osteomyelitis ……62
□ 骨髄腔 medullary cavity ……40
□ 骨折 [bone] fracture …… 16, 62, 64
□ 圧迫―― compression fracture ……64
□ 開放―― open fracture …… 63, 64
□ 完全―― complete fracture ……64
□ 陥没―― depressed fracture ……63
□ 亀裂―― fissured fracture; linear fracture ……63
□ 斜―― oblique fracture ……63
□ 大腿骨頸部―― femoral neck fracture ……64
□ 単純―― simple fracture …… 64, 63
□ 橈骨遠位端―― distal radius fracture ……64
□ 剥離―― sprain fracture; avulsion fracture ……63
□ 病的―― pathologic fracture …… 62, 64
□ 疲労―― fatigue fracture ……64
□ 不完全―― incomplete fracture ……64
□ 複雑―― compound fracture …… 64, 63
□ 粉砕―― comminuted fracture ……63
□ 閉鎖―― closed fracture …… 63, 64
□ 横―― transverse fracture ……63
□ 螺旋―― twisted fracture; spiral fracture ……63
□ 若木―― green-stick fracture ……64
□ 骨粗鬆症 osteoporosis …… 62, 64
□ 骨端 epiphysis ……40
□ 骨端線損傷 epiphyseal injury ……64
□ 骨盤神経節 pelvic ganglion ……56
□ 骨盤内臓神経 pelvic splanchnic nerve ……57
□ 骨膜 periosteum …… 36, 40
□ 固定器具 immobilizer ……88
□ 〔訓練用〕固定式自転車 stational bicycle ……16
□ こぶ lump ……76
□ ゴルフ肘 golfer's elbow ……92

さ

□ 座位 sitting position ……32
□ 催眠薬 narcotics ……71
□ 作業療法 occupational therapy ……17
□ 作業療法士 occupational therapist (OT) 2, 13, 14, 17
□ 鎖骨 clavicle; collarbone …… 33, 37, 38
□ 坐骨 ischium ……38
□ 坐骨神経 ischial nerve ……55
□ 挫傷 strain ……86
□ 三角筋 deltoid muscle …… 46, 48, 50
□ 三角巾 sling ……88
□ 三頭筋 triceps muscle ……48
□ 指圧手技 chiropractic manipulation …… 69, 71
□ シーバー病 Sever's disease ……92
□ 紫外線 ultraviolet light ……16
□ 耳下腺 parotid gland …… 56, 57
□ 軸骨格 axial skeleton ……37
□ 軸索 axon ……52
□ 軸椎 axis ……39
□ 刺激 stimulus …… 6, 52, 53
□ 指骨 bones of fingers; bones of toes ……37
□ 自己免疫疾患 autoimmune disorder ……76
□ 四肢麻痺 tetraplegia; quadriplegia ……95
□ 矢状面 sagittal plane …… 22, 23
□ 自助具 self-help device ……16
□ 耳神経節 otic ganglion ……57
□ 姿勢 posture …… 6
□ 姿勢不安定 postural instability ……99
□ 視聴覚教材 audio-visual aid ……19
□ 膝蓋骨 patella …… 37, 38, 42, 49, 88
□ 膝蓋靱帯 patellar ligament ……49
□ 膝蓋軟骨軟化症 chondromalacia patellae ……92
□ 失行症 apraxia …… 107
□ 失語症 aphasia …… 106, 107, 121, 124
□ 運動性―― motor aphasia …… 107
□ 感覚性―― sensory aphasia …… 107
□ 受容性―― receptive aphasia …… 122
□ 表出性―― expressive aphasia …… 122
□ 湿性咳嗽 productive cough …… 111
□ 自動運動 active movement ……84
□ 児童福祉施設 child welfare institution ……18
□ 児童養護施設 infant nursing facility …… 123
□ シナプス synapse ……52
□ 視能訓練士 orthoptist (ORT) ……14
□ 自発的回復 spontaneous return …… 104
□ 自閉症 autism …… 19, 124
□ 自閉症スペクトラム障害 autistic spectrum disorder(s) …… 122, 124
□ 脂肪細胞 adipose cell ……77
□ 脂肪塞栓症 fat embolism ……65
□ 脂肪体 fat pad ……42

INTRODUCTION CHAPTER I CHAPTER II CHAPTER III CHAPTER IV APPENDIX

□ 脂肪に富む肉　fatty meat ···· 4
□ シムス位　Sims' position ···· 31
□ 社会的リハビリテーション　social rehabilitation　14
□ 社会復帰　rehabilitation ···· 13
□ 斜骨折　oblique fracture ···· 63
□ 車軸関節　pivot joint ···· 43
□ 尺骨　ulna ···· 37, 38, 49
□ 尺骨神経　ulnar nerve ···· 55
□ 収縮する　contract ···· 45
□ 重症度　severity ···· 19, 94
□ 十二指腸　duodenum ···· 7
□ 修復　repair ···· 94, 95
□ 手根骨　carpal bone ···· 37, 38
□ 手掌　palm ···· 33
□ 樹状突起　dendrite ···· 52
□ 出血　hemorrhage ···· 106
□ 出血性の　hemorrhagic ···· 106
□ 出生時欠損　birth defect ···· 18
□ 手背部　dorsum of hand ···· 33
□ 受容器　receptor ···· 52
□ 受容性言語　receptive language ···· 120
□ 受容性失語〔症〕　receptive aphasia ···· 122
□ 潤滑　lubrication ···· 75
□ 循環　circulation ···· 53
□ 準備運動　warm-up ···· 8
□ 消化　digestion ···· 53
□ 障害　disability ···· 2, 4, 17
□ 障害　handicap ···· 17
□ 障害　impairment ···· 16, 17
□ 傷害　injury ···· 12
□ 上頸神経節　superior cervical ganglion ···· 56
□ 掌屈　palmar flexion ···· 25, 27
□ 小結節　nodule ···· 76
□ 上行性伝導路　ascending conduction route ···· 54
□ 踵骨　calcaneus bone ···· 46, 83
□ 踵骨棘　heel spurs; bone spurs ···· 92
□ 踵骨腱　calcaneal tendon ···· 46, 49
□ 踵骨骨端炎　calcaneal apophysitis ···· 92
□ 上肢　upper extremity; upper limb ···· 37
□ 硝子軟骨　hyaline cartilage ···· 77
□ 上伸筋支帯　superior extensor retinaculum ···· 49
□ 上大静脈　superior vena cava ···· 7
□ 上唾液核　superior salivatory nucleus ···· 57
□ 小腸　small intestine ···· 7, 56
□ 上腸間膜神経節　superior mesenteric ganglion ···· 56
□ 小脳　cerebellum ···· 52, 55, 57
□ 踵部　heel ···· 33
□ 上方　superior ···· 22, 23
□ 静脈　vein ···· 6, 7
□ 上腕骨　humerus; upper arm bone ···· 38, 49, 85
□ 上腕二頭筋　biceps brachii ···· 46, 49
□ 上腕三頭筋　triceps brachii ···· 49
□ 除去する　eliminate ···· 13
□ 職業安定所　employment security office ···· 14
□ 職業カウンセリング　vocational counseling ···· 14
□ 職業訓練　vocational training ···· 14
□ 職業的リハビリテーション　vocational rehabilitation ···· 14
□ 職業評価　vocational assessment ···· 14
□ 職業復帰カウンセラー　vocational rehabilitation (VR) counselor ···· 14
□ 食道　esophagus ···· 57
□ 食道嚥下障害　esophageal dysphagia ···· 118
□ 食道の　esophageal ···· 118
□ 職場　workplace ···· 14
□ 書字障害　dysgraphia ···· 122
□ 自律神経系　autonomic nervous system (ANS) ···· 53, 56, 57
□ 心因性嚥下障害　psychogenic dysphagia ···· 117
□ 人格変容　personality change ···· 104
□ 心筋　cardiac muscle ···· 45, 48
□ 心筋細胞　cardiac cell ···· 48
□ 伸筋支帯　extensor retinaculum ···· 46
□ 神経　nerve ···· 57
□ 　顔面――　facial nerve ···· 56
□ 　脛骨――　tibial nerve ···· 55
□ 　坐骨――　ischial nerve ···· 55
□ 　尺骨――　ulnar nerve ···· 55
□ 　正中――　median nerve ···· 55
□ 　脊髄――　spinal nerve ···· 54
□ 　舌咽――　hypoglossal nerve ···· 56
□ 　総腓骨――　common fibular (peroneal) nerve　55
□ 　大腿――　femoral nerve ···· 55
□ 　動眼――　oculomotor nerve ···· 56

□ 橈骨―― radial nerve ……55
□ 脳―― cranial nerve ……54
□ 迷走―― vagus nerve ……56
□ 肋間―― intercostal nerve ……55
□ 神経系 nervous system …… 52, 53
□ 神経細胞 nerve cell ……52
□ 神経終末 nerve ending …… 68, 69
□ 心血管系 cardiovascular system …… 8
□ 進行性運動障害 progressive movement disorder 99
□ 深在の deep ……23
□ シンスプリント shin splint ……92
□ 振せん tremor …… 99, 100
□ 振せん麻痺 parkinsonism ……99
□ 心臓 heart …… 6, 56, 57
□ 腎臓 kidney…… 6, 56, 57
□ 靭帯 ligament …… 6
□ 身体障害 physical disability ……13
□ 身体的奇形 physical deformity…… 123
□ 伸展 extension …… 25, 26, 27, 29, 30
□ 心理社会的剥奪 psychosocial deprivation …… 123
□ 随意筋 voluntary muscle …… 45, 47
□ 膵臓 pancreas……56
□ 水平面 horizontal plane…… 22, 23
□ 睡眠障害 sleep disorder …… 107
□ ズーデック骨萎縮 Sudeck's atrophy ……65
□ スプリント splint …… 16, 77, 88
□ スポーツ医 sports medicine doctor; sports physician ……14
□ スポーツ傷害 sports injury ……83
□ 生活の質 quality of life ……16
□ 整形外科的な orthopedic ……16
□ 正座 kneeling on the floor……32
□ 性質 nature……19
□ 生殖 reproduction ……53
□ 生殖器 genitalia ……56
□ 精神衛生上の問題 mental health issue ……19
□ 精神障害 mental disorder…… 107
□ 精神遅滞 mental disability …… 122
□ 精神保健福祉士 psychiatric social worker (PSW) 14
□ 声帯 vocal cord …… 121
□ 生体自己制御 biofeedback ……69
□ 正中神経 median nerve……55
□ 正中面 median plane …… 22, 23
□ 生命維持器官 vital organ …… 6
□ 世界保健機関 World Health Organization (WHO) 2,3
□ 脊髄 spinal cord …… 52, 53, 54, 55, 57
□ 脊髄神経 spinal nerve ……54
□ 脊髄損傷 spinal cord injury ……94
□ 脊柱 spine; vertebral column …… 37, 38, 39, 40
□ 脊椎管 spinal canal; vertebral canal…… 94, 95
□ 舌咽神経 hypoglossal nerve ……56
□ 舌下腺 sublingual gland …… 56, 57
□ 接合部 synapse ……52
□ 舌骨 hyoid bone; tongue bone …… 37, 50
□ 接触感染性の contagious …… 111, 112
□ 切断 amputation……16
□ 腺 gland ……52
□ 線維芽細胞 fibrous cell ……77
□ 線維組織 fibrous tissue ……85
□ 線維膜 fibrous articular capsule ……42
□ 前額面 frontal plane ……23
□ 前鋸筋 serratus anterior muscle …… 46, 48
□ 前脛骨筋 anterior tibial muscle …… 46, 48, 49
□ 仙骨 sacrum …… 37, 38, 39, 42, 55
□ 仙骨神経叢 sacral plexus ……55
□ 前斜角筋 scalenus anterior muscle ……50
□ 前十字靱帯損傷 anterior cruciate ligament injury 92
□ 仙椎 sacral vertebrae ……39
□ 先天性の congenital …… 117, 118
□ 前方 anterior …… 22, 23
□ 前方脱臼 anterior dislocation ……85
□ 専門家 professional …… 2
□ 創外固定 external skeletal fixation ……65
□ 装具 brace …… 16, 77, 88
□ 総腓骨神経 common fibular (peroneal) nerve……55
□ 僧帽筋 musculus trapezius; trapezius muscle …… 46, 48, 50
□ ソーシャルワーカー social worker (SW)……14
□ 側臥位 side-lying position ……31
□ 足関節 ankle joint ……33
□ 足関節捻挫 sprained ankle …… 86, 92
□ 側屈 lateral flexion; lateral bending …… 25, 30
□ 足根骨 tarsal bone …… 37, 38
□ 塞栓 embolus …… 105, 106

□ 塞栓性〔脳〕卒中　embolic stroke ··········· 105
□ 足底筋膜炎　plantar fasciitis ··········· 92
□ 足底屈　plantar flexion ··········· 87
□ 足底部　sole ··········· 33
□ 足背部　instep ··········· 33
□ 鼠径部　groin ··········· 33
□ 鼠径部損傷　groin pull ··········· 92
□ 鼠径部捻挫　groin strain ··········· 92
□ 鼠径部裂傷　groin tear ··········· 92
□ 組織　tissue ··········· 36
□ 疎性結合組織　areolar tissue ··········· 77
□ 外返し　eversion ··········· 25, 28
□ 損傷　injury ··········· 12

た

□ 第一頸椎　atlas ··········· 39
□ 第二頸椎　axis ··········· 39
□ 大円筋　teres major muscle ··········· 46
□ 大胸筋　major pectoral muscle ··········· 46, 50
□ 代謝　metabolism ··········· 4
□ 対称的な　symmetrical ··········· 76
□ 体操　gymnastics ··········· 85
□ 大腿骨　femur ··········· 37, 38, 42
□ 大腿骨頸部骨折　femoral neck fracture ··········· 64
□ 大腿神経　femoral nerve ··········· 55
□ 大腿二頭筋　biceps femoris muscle ··········· 46
□ 大腿四頭筋　quadriceps ··········· 88
□ 大腸　large intestine ··········· 7, 57
□ 大殿筋　gluteus maximus muscle ··········· 46
□ 大転子　greater trochanter ··········· 38
□ 大動脈　aorta ··········· 7
□ 大脳　cerebrum ··········· 52, 55, 57
□ 対立　opposition ··········· 25, 27
□ 楕円関節　ellipsoid joint; condylar joint ··········· 43
□ 脱臼　dislocation ··········· 85, 88
□ 他動運動　passive movement ··········· 84
□ 多発〔性〕硬化〔症〕　multiple sclerosis ··········· 19
□ 打撲傷　bruising ··········· 85
□ 短期記憶減退　reduced short-term memory ··· 107
□ 短骨　short bone ··········· 40
□ 単純骨折　simple fracture ··········· 64, 63
□ たんぱく尿　proteinuria ··········· 62
□ 断面　plane ··········· 23
□ 恥骨　pubis ··········· 38
□ 緻密質　compact substance; compact bone ··········· 40
□ 注意欠陥多動性障害　attention deficit hyperactivity disorder (ADHD) ··········· 122
□ 中頸神経節　middle cervical ganglion ··········· 56
□ 中間の　intermediate ··········· 23
□ 中斜角筋　scalenus medius muscle ··········· 50
□ 中手骨　metacarpal bone ··········· 37
□ 中枢神経系　central nervous system (CNS) ··········· 53, 54, 55, 57
□ 中足骨　metatarsal bone ··········· 37
□ 中殿筋　gluteus medius muscle ··········· 46
□ 腸　intestine ··········· 6, 7, 45
□ 超音波　ultrasound ··········· 69
□ 聴覚障害　hearing loss; hearing impairment　19, 122
□ 聴覚喪失　hearing loss ··········· 122
□ 腸骨　ilium ··········· 38
□ 長骨　long bone ··········· 40
□ 長座位　long sitting position ··········· 32
□ 蝶番関節　hinge joint ··········· 43
□ 長頭　long head ··········· 49
□ 長母指屈筋　long flexor of toes ··········· 49
□ 調和運動障害　impaired coordination ··········· 100
□ 直腸　rectum ··········· 7
□ 鎮静薬　sedative ··········· 71
□ 鎮痛薬　analgesic ··········· 71
□ 椎間孔　intervertebral foramen ··········· 39
□ 椎間板　intervertebral disc; vertebral disc ··· 39, 40
□ 椎骨　vertebra ··········· 37, 39
□ 対麻痺　paraplegia ··········· 95
□ 杖　walking stick ··········· 77
□ 底屈　plantar flexion ··········· 25, 28
□ 手関節　wrist joint ··········· 33
□ テニス肘　tennis elbow ··········· 92
□ 頭蓋　cranium; skull ··········· 37, 38, 55
□ 動眼神経　oculomotor nerve ··········· 56
□ 瞳孔　pupil ··········· 57
□ 橈骨　radius ··········· 37, 38, 49
□ 橈骨遠位端骨折　distal radius fracture ··········· 64
□ 橈骨神経　radial nerve ··········· 55
□ 頭側の　cranial ··········· 22, 23

□ 頭頂部　parietal part ……33
□ 疼痛　pain ……68
□ 疼痛のある　aching ……69
□ 糖尿病　diabetes …… 106
□ 頭板状筋　splenius capitis muscle ……50
□ 動脈　artery …… 6, 7
□ 動脈壁　artery wall …… 105
□ 動脈瘤　aneurysm …… 105, 106
□ 投与量　dose …… 100
□ 特異的言語発達障害　specific language impairment (SLI) …… 122
□ 特別支援学級　special support class …… 123
□ 徒手整復　manipulation …… 65, 86
□ 徒手的整復術　open reduction ……65
□ 突出　protrusion, protraction …… 25, 26
□ ドパミン　dopamine (DM) …… 99, 100

な

□ 内果　medial malleolus …… 33, 49
□ 内固定　internal fixation ……65
□ 内旋　internal rotation; medial rotation …… 25, 29
□ 内臓　internal organ ……45
□ 内臓頭蓋　viscerocranium ……37
□ 内側外転　medial abduction ……27
□ 内側広筋　vastus medialis muscle ……49
□ 内側上果炎　medial epicondylitis ……92
□ 内側頭　medial head ……49
□ 内側の　medial …… 22, 23
□ 内転　adduction …… 25, 27, 29
□ 内反　varus ……25
□ 内分泌腺　endocrine gland ……53
□ 軟骨　cartilage …… 36, 40
□ 難聴　hearing loss; hearing impairment … 19, 122
□ 日常生活動作　activities of daily living (ADL) ……18
□ 日課　routine work ……17
□ 二頭筋　biceps muscle ……48
□ 入院患者〔の〕　in-patient ……13
□ ニューロン　neuron ……53
□ 認知症　dementia ……19
□ 認知障害　cognitive difficulty …… 104
□ 認知的変化　cognitive change ……17
□ 粘液　mucus …… 111, 112
□ 捻挫　sprain ……88
□ 脳　brain ……6, 54
□ 脳血管　cerebral artery ……56
□ 脳血管障害　cerebrovascular accident (CVA) … 104
□ 脳梗塞　cerebral infarction …… 121
□ 脳神経　cranial nerve ……54
□ 脳しんとう　concussion ……92
□ 脳卒中　stroke …… 16, 19, 104, 106
□ 脳頭蓋　brain case; neurocranium ……37

は

□ パーキンソン病　Parkinson's disease (PD) ……99
□ ハーブ療法　herbal remedy ……69
□ 肺　lung …… 6, 45, 57
□ 肺気腫　emphysema …… 111, 112
□ 背屈　dorsiflexion; dorsal flexion …… 25, 27, 28
□ 排泄　excretion ……53
□ 背側の　dorsal …… 22, 23
□ 肺胞　alveolus …… 6
□ 廃用性筋萎縮　disuse atrophy …… 123
□ 剥がれ落ちる　flake off ……85
□ 白線　linea alba ……46
□ 剥離骨折　sprain fracture; avulsion fracture ……63
□ 発声障害　dysphonia …… 121, 124
□ 発声障害　speech disorder …… 124
□ 発達性協調運動障害　developmental incoordination …… 122
□ 発達性言語遅滞　developmental language disorder …… 122
□ 発達遅滞　developmental disability …… 123
□ 鍼　acupuncture ……69
□ 腫れ　swelling ……62
□ 破裂　rupture …… 105
□ 半関節　amphiarthrosis ……42
□ 半月板　meniscus ……88
□ 半月板損傷　meniscus injury ……92
□ 半座位　semi-sitting position ……32
□ 反射弓　reflex arc ……52
□ 半側臥位　half side-lying position ……31
□ 半腹臥位　semiprone position ……31
□ 反復性脱臼　recurrent dislocation ……86
□ 半膜様筋　semimembranosus muscle …… 46, 48

□ 非観血的整復術　closed reduction …… 65
□ 腓骨　fibula …… 37, 38
□ 尾骨　coccyx …… 37, 38, 39
□ 膝関節　knee joint …… 33
□ 肘関節　elbow joint …… 33, 49
□ 非ステロイド性抗炎症薬　non-steroidal anti-inflammatory drugs (NSAIDs) …… 69, 70
□ 尾側の　caudal …… 22, 23
□ ビタミン欠乏障害　vitamin deficiency disorder …… 62
□ 左回旋　left rotation …… 25
□ 尾椎　coccygeal vertebrae …… 39
□ 鼻粘膜　nasal mucosa …… 57
□ 皮膚　skin …… 6
□ 腓腹筋　gastrocnemius …… 46, 49
□ 表在の　superficial …… 23
□ 表出性言語　expressive language …… 120
□ 表出性失語〔症〕　expressive aphasia …… 122
□ 病訴　complaint …… 117, 118
□ 表層筋　outer muscle …… 46
□ 表層細胞　superficial cell …… 77
□ 病的骨折　pathologic fracture …… 62, 64
□ ヒラメ筋　soleus muscle …… 46, 48, 49
□ 疲労骨折　fatigue fracture …… 64
□ ファウラー位　Fowler's position …… 32
□ フォルクマン拘縮　Volkmann's contracture …… 65
□ 不完全骨折　incomplete fracture …… 64
□ 不規則骨　irregular bone …… 40
□ 復位　reposition …… 27
□ 腹臥位, 伏臥位　prone position …… 31
□ 腹腔神経節　celiac ganglion …… 56, 57
□ 副交感神経系　parasympathetic nervous system (PNS) …… 53, 57
□ 複雑骨折　compound fracture …… 64, 63
□ 副子, 副木　splint …… 16, 77, 88
□ 副腎　adrenal gland …… 56
□ 腹側の　ventral …… 22, 23
□ 腹直筋　rectus abdominis muscle …… 46
□ 不随意筋　involuntary muscle …… 45, 47
□ 不動結合　synarthrosis …… 42
□ 粉砕骨折　comminuted fracture …… 63
□ 分回し　circumduction …… 29
□ 平滑筋　smooth muscle …… 45, 47
□ 平滑筋細胞　smooth muscle cell …… 47
□ 閉鎖骨折　closed fracture …… 63, 64
□ 閉鎖整復　closed reduction …… 86
□ 平面関節　plane joint …… 43
□ 変形　deformity …… 62
□ 変形性関節症　osteoarthritis (OA) …… 75, 76, 78
□ 変色　discoloration …… 62
□ 片側不全麻痺　hemiparesis …… 106
□ 扁平骨　flat bone …… 40
□ 膀胱　urinary bladder …… 56, 57
□ 縫工筋　sartorius muscle …… 46
□ 包帯　bandage …… 88
□ ホームヘルパー　home helper …… 14
□ 保健師　public health nurse (PHN) …… 14
□ 母趾外転筋　abductor muscle of great toe …… 49
□ 補助装具　assistive device …… 77
□ 補助的鎮痛薬　adjuvant analgesics …… 69, 70
□ 保存療法　conservative treatment …… 77, 83
□ 補填する　compensate for …… 17
□ 骨　bone …… 6, 36, 40, 77, 36

ま

□ 麻酔薬　narcotics …… 69, 71
□ 末梢血管　peripheral blood vessel …… 56
□ 末梢神経系　peripheral nervous system (PNS) …… 53, 54, 55, 57
□ 松葉杖　crutch …… 16
□ 麻痺　paralysis; numbness …… 16, 85, 95
□ 麻薬　narcotics …… 71
□ 慢性気管支炎　chronic bronchitis …… 111
□ 慢性閉塞性肺疾患　chronic obstructive pulmonary disease (COPD) …… 111, 112
□ 慢性腰痛　chronic low back pain …… 68
□ 右回旋　right rotation …… 25
□ ミネラル　mineral …… 36
□ 身ぶり　gesture …… 120
□ 無菌壊死　aseptic necrosis …… 65
□ 無動　akinesia …… 99
□ 瞑想　meditation …… 69
□ 迷走神経　vagus nerve …… 56
□ 免疫系　immune system …… 76, 78
□ 毛細血管　capillary …… 6, 7

□ 盲腸　cecum …… 7
□ 毛様体神経節　ciliary ganglion …… 57

や

□ 遊走肋骨　floating rib …… 38
□ 癒合　fusion …… 70
□ 腰神経叢　lumbar plexus …… 55
□ 腰椎　lumbar vertebra …… 39, 55
□ 腰痛　low back pain …… 69
□ 翼口蓋神経節　sphenopalatine ganglion …… 57
□ 横骨折　transverse fracture …… 63

ら

□ 螺旋骨折　twisted fracture; spiral fracture …… 63
□ 楽観的　optimistic …… 94
□ ランナー膝　runner's knee …… 92
□ リウマチ　rheumatism …… 75
□ リウマチ小結節　rheumatoid nodule …… 76
□ 理学療法　physical therapy …… 16
□ 理学療法士　physical therapist (PT) …… 2, 13, 14, 16
□ 立位　standing position …… 32
□ リトルリーグ肘　little league elbow …… 92
□ リハビリテーション　rehabilitation …… 13
□ リハビリテーション医　physiatrist …… 13, 14
□ リハビリテーション専門病院　rehabilitation hospital …… 14
□ リン酸　phosphorus …… 36
□ 臨床心理士　clinical psychologist (CP) …… 14
□ 涙腺　lacrimal gland …… 57
□ 冷却　ice …… 84
□ 冷湿布　cold pack …… 16, 69
□ レセプタ　receptor …… 52
□ 肋間神経　intercostal nerve …… 55
□ 肋骨　rib …… 37, 38

わ

□ 若木骨折　green-stick fracture …… 64
□ 腕神経叢　brachial plexus …… 55

・本書各Chapterの日本語訳やExerciseの解答をまとめた教授用資料をご希望の方にお分けします（ただし学校教材として利用されている学生の方は除きます）。
・教授用資料は，冊子（郵送）またはPDF（メール添付）でお送りいたします。
・ご希望の方は必ず**書面（FAX, E-mailも可）にて，氏名・勤務先または学校名・送付先住所を明記**の上，下記へお申し込みください。

申込先：メジカルビュー社編集部　医学英語書籍担当者
〒162-0845　東京都新宿区市谷本村町2-30
FAX　03-5228-2062
E-MAIL　ed@medicalview.co.jp

リハビリテーションの基礎英語　第3版

2009年　4月10日　第1版　第1刷発行
2016年　1月　1日　改訂第2版第1刷発行
2018年　3月10日　第3版第2刷発行

■企画・構成・編著　清水雅子　しみず まさこ
■英文監修　Timothy Minton　ティモシー ミントン
■PT・OT監修　三木貴弘　みき たかひろ
上　梓　かみ あずさ

■発行者　鳥羽清治

■発行所　株式会社メジカルビュー社
〒162-0845 東京都新宿区市谷本村町2-30
電話　03 (5228) 2050（代表）
ホームページ http://www.medicalview.co.jp/
営業部　FAX 03 (5228) 2059
E-mail　eigyo@medicalview.co.jp
編集部　FAX 03 (5228) 2062
E-mail　ed@medicalview.co.jp

■印刷所　加藤文明社

ISBN978-4-7583-0961-5 C3047